G000122597

MICRO AND NANOMANUFACTURING RESEARCH

MATERIALS AND MANUFACTURING TECHNOLOGY

J. PAULO DAVIM - SERIES EDITOR -
UNIVERSITY. OF AVEIRO, AVEIRO, PORTUGAL

Drilling of Composite Materials
J. Paulo Davim (Editor)
2009. ISBN: 978-1-60741-163-5 (Hardcover)
2009. ISBN: 978-1-60876-584-3 (E-book)

Artificial Intelligence in Manufacturing Research
J. Paulo Davim (Editor)
2010. ISBN: 978-1-60876-214-9 (Hardcover)
2011. ISBN: 978-1-61761-564-1 (E-book)

Metal Cutting: Research Advances
J. Paulo Davim (Editor)
2010. ISBN: 978-1-60876-207-1 (Hardcover)
2010. ISBN: 978-1-61122-573-0 (E-book)

Tribology Research Advances
J. Paulo Davim (Editor)
2011. ISBN: 978-1-60692-885-1 (Hardcover)

Tribology of Composite Materials
J. Paulo Davim (Editor)
2010. ISBN: 978-1-61668-319-1 (Hardcover)
2012. ISBN: 978-1-62100-999-3 (Softcover)
2010. ISBN: 978-1-61324-772-3 (E-book)

Micro and Nanomanufacturing Research
J. Paulo Davim (Editor)
2010. ISBN: 978-1-61668-488-4 (Hardcover)
2012. ISBN: 978-1-61942-003-8 (Softcover)
2010. ISBN: 978-1-61324-366-4 (E-book)

Medical Device Manufacturing
Mark J. Jackson and J. Paulo Davim (Editors)
2011. ISBN: 978-1-61209-715-2 (Hardcover)

Metal Matrix Composites
J. Paulo Davim (Editor)
2011. ISBN: 978-1-61209-771-8 (Hardcover)

Biomedical Tribology

J. Paulo Davim (Editor)

2011. ISBN: 978-1-61470-056-2 (Hardcover)
2011. ISBN: 978-1-61470-153-8 (E-book)

MATERIALS AND MANUFACTURING TECHNOLOGY

MICRO AND NANOMANUFACTURING RESEARCH

J. PAULO DAVIM
EDITOR

Nova Science Publishers, Inc.
New York

NOTICE TO THE READER

The Publisher has taken reasonable care in the preparation of this book, but makes no expressed or implied warranty of any kind and assumes no responsibility for any errors or omissions. No liability is assumed for incidental or consequential damages in connection with or arising out of information contained in this book. The Publisher shall not be liable for any special, consequential, or exemplary damages resulting, in whole or in part, from the readers' use of, or reliance upon, this material.

Independent verification should be sought for any data, advice or recommendations contained in this book. In addition, no responsibility is assumed by the publisher for any injury and/or damage to persons or property arising from any methods, products, instructions, ideas or otherwise contained in this publication.

This publication is designed to provide accurate and authoritative information with regard to the subject matter covered herein. It is sold with the clear understanding that the Publisher is not engaged in rendering legal or any other professional services. If legal or any other expert assistance is required, the services of a competent person should be sought. FROM A DECLARATION OF PARTICIPANTS JOINTLY ADOPTED BY A COMMITTEE OF THE AMERICAN BAR ASSOCIATION AND A COMMITTEE OF PUBLISHERS.

Additional color graphics may be available in the e-book version of this book.

LIBRARY OF CONGRESS CATALOGING-IN-PUBLICATION DATA

Micro and nanomanufacturing research / editor, J. Paulo Davim.
    p. cm.
 Includes bibliographical references and index.
 ISBN 978-1-61942-003-8 (softcover)
 1. Micromachining. 2. Nanotechnology. I. Davim, J. Paulo.
 TJ1191.5.M498 2010
 620'.5--dc22
                        2010015614

Published by Nova Science Publishers, Inc. ✦ *New York*

CONTENTS

PREFACE

Manufacturing on the small scale is the technology for production of miniaturized components and functional products. Micro and nanomanufacturing is a key to the development of modern industry in many countries. Nowadays, the use of microcomponents and miniaturized functional products from metals, polymers, ceramics, composites and advanced materials has increased in various areas of science and technology due to their special properties, with applications in microelectronic, biomedical, aircraft, automotive, defence and aerospace, as well other advanced industries.

This book presents research and reviews studies on micro and nanomanufacturing. The first chapter provides information on micromanufacturing using x-ray lithographic technologies. Chapter 2 focuses on mechanistic modelling approach for micromilling cutting forces. Chapter 3 contains a study on surface quality in micromilling. Chapter 4 focuses on numerical simulation and experimental validation when precision radial turning AISI 1045 steel. Subsequently, the chapter 5 deals with the effect of cutting speed on cutting forces and surface finish when micro turning polyamides. Chapter 6 discusses pulsed droplet micromachining of abrasive materials. Chapter 7 contains some aspects of non-conventional micro machining technology-an overview. Finally, the last chapter of this research book focuses on manufacturing and application of micro/nano fluidic devices.

The present research book can be used for final undergraduate engineering course (for example, mechanical, manufacturing, materials etc) or as a subject on micro and nanomanufacturing at the postgraduate level. Also, this book can serve as a useful reference for academics, manufacturing researchers, mechanical, manufacturing and physics engineers, professional in related industries with micro and nanotechnology.

Editor acknowledges his gratitude to Nova Publishers for the opportunity to present this material and for their professional support. Finally, the editor would like to thank all the chapter authors for making their research available for this work.

In: Micro and Nanomanufacturing Research
Editor: J. Paulo Davim

Chapter 1

MICROMANUFACTURING USING X-RAY LITHOGRAPHIC TECHNOLOGIES

M. J. Jackson[*]

MET, College of Technology, Purdue University, West Lafayette,
Indiana 47907, US

ABSTRACT

There has been a rapid development in microfabrication technology driven by the market need for low-cost consumer products such as portable telecommunications equipment, computers and healthcare diagnostics. Much of the technology used for these is based on production of silicon semiconductors. An interest in non-silicon based technologies started to grow in the early 1980s with the development of a German fabrication process known as LIGA, an acronym for Lithography (LIthographie), electroplating (Galvanoformung), molding (Abformung). It originated at the Karlsruhe Nuclear Research Laboratory in Germany. Since then a number of groups, mainly in Germany and the US have been active in developing the process to make precision microcomponents for a range of products such as microspectrometers, fibre-optic wave guides, micro-reactors, and microfluidic devices. A few of these have been manufactured on a large scale and placed on the market. LIGA is often used to fabricate the components, which were then integrated with other components. This paper describes the essential principle of the LIGA process and explains how x-ray lithography is used for micromanufacturing small parts.

[*] Corresponding author: E-mail: jacksomj@purdue.edu

1. INTRODUCTION

The most active groups developing and using the LIGA process are the Sandia National Laboratories at Livermore, the Centre for Advanced Microstructures and Devices (CAMD) at the Louisiana State University at Baton Rouge, in the US, Institut fur Mikrostrukturtechnik (FZK) Karlsruhe and Antwenderzentrum (BESSY), Berlin in Germany. In addition the work done in the UK at Central Microstructure Facility at the CCLRC's Rutherford Appleton Laboratory using the national synchrotron at Daresbury as part of a European network programme has advanced fabrication techniques in mask and resist development. Initial steps toward commercialization has been made by two companies in the US: Axsun; and International Mezzo, who provide commercial LIGA services [1-6].

Extensive papers and reviews on microfabrication technologies have been published. Two examples of which are: 'The Fundamentals of Microfabrication' by Madou 2002 [7], and 'Microfabrication using Synchrotron Radiation' by Tolfree in 1998 [8]. These and others can be found in the literature and cover most of the relevant principles and issues associated with the development and exploitation of the technologies. The technique is known as deep X-ray lithography (DXRL), is similar to lithographic processes, ultimately limited in line-width by the wavelength of the illuminating radiation. The conversion from a 2-D pattern to a 3-D structure is dependent on a number of factors. These will be examined below.

There are multiple types of lithography, including UV, deep UV, X-ray and electron-beam lithography. Currently, for non-silicon-based materials, the highest precision can be achieved using DXRL with parallel, high energy X-rays from synchrotron radiation sources (SRS). It is the increased access provided by the large number (>80) of synchrotron now operating world-wide, coupled to availability of low solubility resists thus reducing exposure time that has encouraged a greater interest in DXRL. This technique still has to find a wider community of users outside of research but it will have a significant role to play in the range of tools and processes required to develop a micro-nanotechnology (MNT) based industry.

Micro-nanotechnology (MNT) is pervasive and will have an impact, sometimes disruptive, on almost every industry sector and through the generation of new products and systems, on the society in general. The universal use of the mobile telephone and ink-jet printer are two well-known examples.

2. X-RAY LITHOGRAPHY

International Business Machines (IBM) first combined electro deposition and x-ray lithography in 1969. They made high-aspect ratio metal structures by plating gold patterns of 20 μm in thickness in a resist that had been exposed to x-rays. The IBM work was an extension of through-mask plating, also pioneered by IBM in 1969, and was directed towards the fabrication of thin film magnetic recording heads. An historical background of lithography was given by Cerrina [9].

The development of the LIGA process was created by the production of small slotted nozzles for uranium isotope separation [10]. Since then, the X-ray lithographic technique has been developed to fabricate a variety of microstructures in materials [11-19]. The potential of

LIGA for the development of microsystems was surveyed by Bacher [20]. Essentially, a three step process, the LIGA technique can be used to make 3D microstructures.

By adding molding techniques the broader implications of x-ray lithography as a means of low-cost manufacturing of a wide variety of micro parts with unprecedented accuracy from various materials can be produced. In Germany, X-ray lithography was originally developed outside of the semiconductor industry.

Early pioneering work in the use of synchrotron radiation for microfabrication was carried out by Henry Guckel at the University of Wisconsin in the US. This included use of the LIGA technique to develop micromotors [21-24].

3. SYNCHROTRON RADIATION (SR)

3.1. General Characteristics

The radiation emitted by relativistic electrons when traversing a magnetic field can be understood from classical electromagnetic theory. Its properties can be expressed by basic equations which are used in the design of synchrotron radiation sources [25-32]. A basic introduction to synchrotron radiation sources is given by Marks [33] and a general review that provides detail of the subject is provided by Turner [34]. The power of the emitted radiation is inversely proportional to the mass of the charged particle, so electrons yield useful quantities of radiation in the visible and X-ray regions of the electromagnetic spectrum.

Centripetal acceleration of highly relativistic charged particles in a magnetic bending field results in the tangential emission of synchrotron radiation over a wide spectrum at every point of the curved particle trajectory. Considering only electrons, the emission pattern is essentially determined by that of a single circulating electron. With reference to Figure 1, the radiation pattern emitted by relativistic electrons can be transformed into the laboratory reference frame resulting in its being compressed in a narrow forward cone, tangential with respect to the electrons circular path. This natural collimation is an important characteristic property of synchrotron radiation. As the electron beam sweeps out the curved path, a continuous fan of radiation results in the horizontal plane while the distribution in the vertical plane is highly collimated.

The opening half-angle of the emission cone of radiation is wavelength-dependent [35] its angular distribution can be approximated by a Gaussian distribution, the width of which is related to the kinetic energy E, and the rest energy (mc2). The natural divergence, δn, is given by:

δn =(mc2)/E

The divergence is an important parameter when considering the use of synchrotron radiation sources for deep X-ray lithography. This has to be as low as possible but is limited to the practical values obtainable for E, which are in the range (1.5-3) GeV for typical national sources; resulting in values for the natural divergence between 0.2 and 0.3 mrad in the X-ray region.

The continuous emission of radiation excites particle oscillations which give rise to a finite extension of the particle beam and corresponding angular deviations with respect to the ideal trajectory. Since the direction of photon emission follows the instantaneous particle direction, an additional angular width, δp, results, which is independent of the natural divergence and when added to the natural divergence it forms the total angular width of the synchrotron radiation and is given by:

$$\text{stot} = (\delta n2 + \delta p2)\ 1/2$$

The electron beam emittance is determined by the particular design of the synchrotron but can be optimized to be similar in magnitude to the natural divergence. A typical value for stot is in the range 0.3-0.4 mrad which leads to a vertical intensity distribution of the beam. At a distance of 10m from the emission point and with a typical beam width of 3-4mm, the beam is seen as a broad radiation fan in the horizontal direction. In calculating the above, the finite width of the beam has been ignored but could be important at the location of the lithography station on an external beam line on a synchrotron. When the beam width is taken into account, the product of beam size, W, and its angular width, δt, is given by the emittance, E:

$$E = W\delta t$$

3.2. Spectral Characteristics

Owing to both longitudinal and transverse oscillations of the circulating electrons, individual components in the frequency spectrum become smeared out, resulting in a continuous spectrum of radiation being emitted from the infra-red to wavelengths shorter than a critical wavelength, λc, in the hard X-ray region.

The spectrum shape is characterised by the electron energy, the beam current and the magnetic field in the accelerator [36]. The spectral distribution from a small elemental arc of radius R along the electron orbit can be described in terms of a critical wavelength, λc (Angstrom units).

$$\lambda c = 18.6/BE\ 2$$

Where E is the electron energy (GeV), B is the bending field (Tesla). The critical wavelength is a useful parameter for characterising emission. It represents the value of wavelength which equally divides the total integrated photon energy. Since the spectrum extends into long wavelengths and the photon energy is inversely proportional to wavelength, the critical wavelength is near the short wavelength end of the spectrum. A typical spectrum from a dipole magnet in which the emission is integrated over the complete fan of radiation is shown in Figure 1. For a source of fixed radius, the radiated power varies as the fourth power of the electron energy.

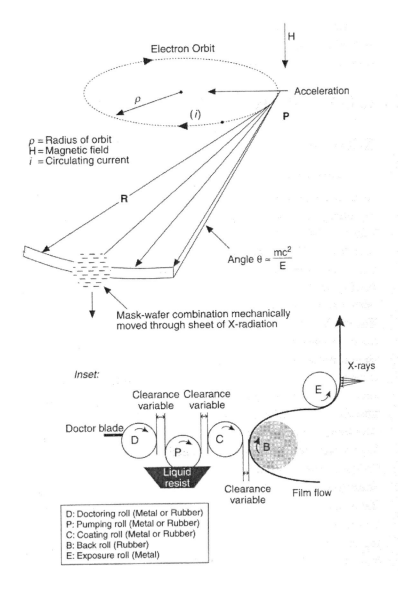

Figure 1. Schematic of an x-ray exposure station with a synchrotron radiation source. The x-ray radiation opening angle, θ, is tangential to the path of the electron describing a line on an intersecting substrate. (After M. Madou, 'Fundamentals of Microfabrication', 2nd Edition, 2002, CRC Press).

3.3. Spectral Brilliance and Brightness

The finite size of the electron beam and the correlation between individual electrons and their orbits is characterised by phase space distributions. The photon flux radiated by the source can be described by a number of different parameters. The spectral flux is the number of photons/s/mrad horizontal emitted into a 0.1% bandwidth, the emission being integrated fully in the vertical plane.

The brightness is the spectral flux per mrad vertical; it therefore has units of photons/s/mrad2 per 0.1% bandwidth. Where the incident beam is focused on a sample, and the source area becomes important, the concept of brilliance - the brightness per unit source area - is used. This has units of photons/s/mrad2/mm2 per 0.1% bandwidth.

The value of brightness or brilliance for any particular synchrotron is dependent on the design of the accelerator and particularly its magnet lattice, a high value of brilliance being required for good resolution [37]. The quality of the radiation source is therefore characterised by its spectral brilliance and the spectral distribution of the emission.

Brightness can be increased by the use of insertion devices like wigglers and undulators, placed in straight sections of the storage ring. These devices have a periodic magnetic structure and therefore produce an oscillatory path of the electrons with enhancement and modification of the radiation. The theory associated with these devices is given in [38,39].

The enhanced penetrating power and beam intensity of the higher energy X-rays resulting from the use of wigglers enables the production of deeper moulds, thus facilitating the manufacture of 3D microstructures. Using data from the Daresbury synchrotron source, parameters required for deep lithography using wiggler radiation were calculated by using software developed at Daresbury Laboratory.

It should be noted that beryllium window can withstand a 1 atmosphere pressure differential across a small diameter (<1 inch). For large area exposures, windows up to 6 cm in diameter have been developed. Beryllium windows age with x-ray exposure and must be replaced periodically. This is one of the limitations of using external X-ray beams and it adds to the overall operational cost.

4. MICROFABRICATION PROCESS

4.1. General

An overview of microlithography, micromachining and microfabrication has been given a SPIE Handbook [9]. A number methods exist for fabricating microstructures but the use of deep X-ray lithography and the LIGA process already referred to above provides the highest dimension precision. Limitations, however in the materials that can be used and the relatively high cost of the process from prototyping to large scale manufacture of components has restricted it wider use. The development of new resists, (SU8) increased knowledge of the process and the wider availability of synchrotron storage rings has awakened renewed interest on LIGA as a viable process technology. The current support for nanotechnology has also raised questions about the boundaries that can be reached for top-down processing.

4.2. LIGA Process

LIGA is a three step process (Figure 2). Although here, we are only considering X-ray based lithography, UV-LIGA and Laser-LIGA techniques have also reached an advanced stage of development. UV–LIGA in particular has encouraged the production of a negative resist known as SU-8 that can also be used in X-ray lithography owing to its increased radiation sensitivity over more commonly used poly-methyl-methacrylate (PMMA) resists, thus reducing exposure time and subsequent costs. The penetrating power of X-rays compared to other longer wavelength radiation allow the fabrication of structures which have vertical dimensions from hundreds of microns to millimetres and horizontal dimensions as small as microns. These 3-D microstructures with high aspect ratios offer a range of microcomponents for many useful applications.

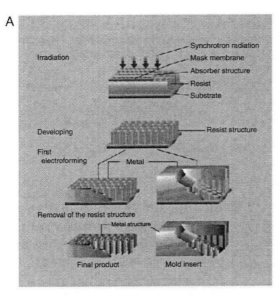

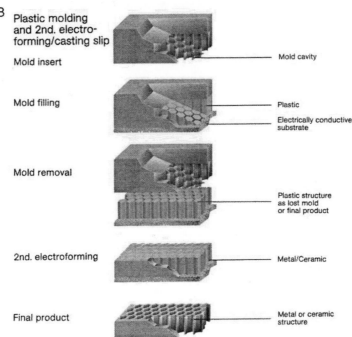

Figure 2. (A) Basic x-ray exposure: (1) x-ray deep-etch lithography and; (2) primary electroforming process; (B) Plastic molding and secondary electroforming process. (After Lehr and Schmidt, 'The LiGA Technique', IMM GmbH, Mainz-Hechstein, 1995).

4.3. Lithography Steps

The first step using X-ray lithography involves exposing a thick layer of resist through a patterned mask to a high-energy beam of X-rays from a Synchrotron. The pattern is etched into the resist substrate by the X-rays. A chemical solvent is used to dissolve away the damaged material resulting in a negative relief replica of the mask pattern. Certain metals can be electrodeposited into the resist mold with after removal of the resist, a free standing metal structure is produced. The metal structure may be a final product, or serve as a mold insert for precision plastic molding. Molded plastic parts may then be final products or lost molds. The plastic mold retains the same shape, size, and form as the original resist structure but is produced quickly. The lost mold may subsequently produce metal parts in a secondary process, or generate ceramic parts using a slip casting process.

4.4. X-ray Lithography

X-ray lithography is basically a shadow printing process in which patterns coated on a mask are transferred into a third dimension in a resist material, normally PMMA. This is subsequently chemical process to dissolve away the volume of material damaged by the x-rays. The quality of the remaining structure is dependent on the beam exposure, the precision of patterning on the mask and the purity and processing of the resist material. Beyond exposure it is the precision of electroforming and micromolding processes that determines the quality of the final product.

Micromachining techniques are changing manufacturing approaches for a wide variety of small parts. Frequently, semiconductor batch microfabrication methods are considered along with traditional serial machining methods. In this sense, x-ray lithography and pseudo x-ray lithography processes are classed as hybrid technologies, bridging semiconductor and classical manufacturing technologies. The ability of x-ray lithography and pseudo x-ray lithography for creating a wide variety of shapes from different materials makes these methods similar to classical machining, with the added benefit of high aspect ratios and absolute tolerances that are possible using lithography and other high-precision mold fabrication techniques.

4.4.1. X-Ray Masks

Good quality, radiation resistant masks are an essential element in lithography. To be highly transmissive to x-rays, the mask substrate must be a low-Z (atomic number) thin membrane. X-ray masks should withstand many exposures without distortion, must be aligned with respect to the sample, and must be rugged. Possible x-ray mask architecture and its assembly with a substrate in an x-ray scanner are shown in Figure 3. The mask shown here has three major components: an absorber, a membrane or mask blank, and a frame. The absorber contains the information to be imaged onto the resist. It is composed of a material with a high atomic number (Z), often gold is used that is patterned to a membrane material with a low Z. The high-Z material absorbs x-rays, whereas the low-Z material transmits x-rays. The frame is robust in relation to the membrane/absorber assembly so that the whole can be handled. The requirements for x-ray masks in x-ray lithography differ substantially from those for the semiconductor industry. A comparison is presented in Table 1. The main difference lies in the thickness of the absorber.

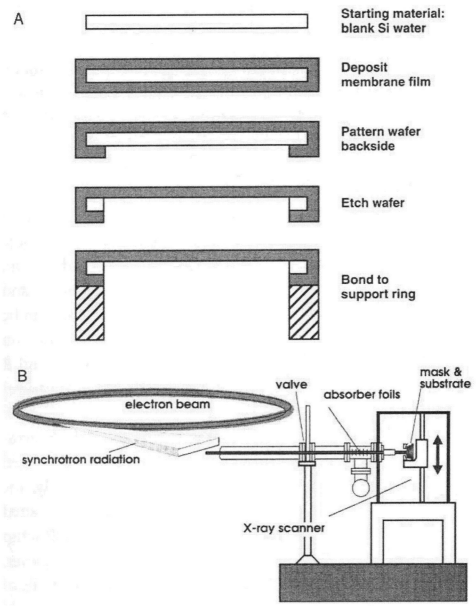

Figure 3. Schematic of a typical x-ray mask (A) and mask and substrate assembly in an x-ray scanner (B). (After M. Madou, 'Fundamentals of Microfabrication', 2nd Edition, 2002, CRC Press).

To achieve high contrast, a very thick absorber (>10 μm vs. 1 μm) and highly transparent mask blanks (transparency >80%) must be used because of the low resist sensitivity and the great depth of the resist. Another difference focuses on the radiation stability of membrane and absorber. For conventional optical lithography, the supporting substrate is a relatively thick, optically flat piece of glass or quartz highly transparent to optical wavelengths. It provides a highly stable (>106 μ m) basis for the thin (0.1 μ m) chrome absorber pattern. In contrast, the x-ray mask consists of a very thin membrane (2 to 4 μ m) of low-Z material carrying a high-Z thick absorber pattern. A single exposure in x-ray lithography results in an exposure dose 100 times higher than in the semiconductor case.

Table 1. Comparison of Masks for use in X-Ray Lithography and the Semiconductor Industry

	Semiconductor lithography	X-ray lithography
Transparency	≥ 50%	≥ 80%
Absorber thickness	± 1 μ m	10 μ m or higher
Field size	50 x 50 mm2	100 x 100 mm2
Radiation resistance	= 1	= 100
Surface roughness	<0.1 μ m	<0.5 μ m
Waviness	<± 1 μ m	<± 1 μ m
	<0.05 μ m	<0.1-0.3 μ m
Dimensional stability	~108 Pa	~108 Pa
Residual membrane stress		

4.4.2. Mask Materials

The low-Z membrane material in an x-ray mask must have a transparency for rays with a critical wavelength, λc, from 0.2 to 0.6 nm of at least 80% and should not scatter those rays. To avoid pattern distortion, the residual stress, σr, in the membrane should be less than 106 N/m2. Mechanical stress in the absorber pattern can cause in-plane distortion of the supporting thin membrane, requiring a high Young's modulus for the membrane material. During one typical lithography step, the masks may be exposed to 1 MJ/cm2 of x-rays. Since most membranes must be very thin for optimal transparency, a compromise has to be found among transparency, strength, and form stability. Important x-ray membrane materials are listed in Table 2. The higher radiation dose in x-ray lithography prevents the use of BN and compound mask blanks that incorporate a polyimide layer. Those mask blanks are perfectly appropriate for classical semiconductor lithography work but will not do for x-ray lithography processes. Mask blanks of metals such as titanium (Ti) and beryllium were specifically developed for x-ray lithography applications because of their resistance to radiation breakdown. In comparing titanium and beryllium membranes, beryllium can have a much greater membrane thickness, d, and still be adequately transparent. For example, a membrane transparency of 80%, essential for adequate exposure of a 500 μ m thick PMMA resist layer, is obtained with a thin 2 μ m titanium film, whereas, with beryllium, a thick 300 μ m membrane achieves the same result. The thicker beryllium membrane permits easier processing and handling. In addition, beryllium has a greater Young's modulus E than titanium and, since it is the product of E and d that determines the amount of mask distortion, distortions due to absorber stress should be much smaller for beryllium blanks. Beryllium is an excellent membrane material for x-ray lithography because of its high transparency and excellent damage resistance. Stoichiometric silicon nitride (Si3N4) used in x-ray mask membranes may contain numerous oxygen impurities, absorbing x-rays and thus producing heat. This heat often suffices to prevent the use of nitride as a good x-ray lithography mask. Single-crystal silicon masks have been made (1 cm square and 0.4 μ m thick, and 10 cm square and 2.5 μ m thick) by electro-chemical etching techniques. For Si and Si3N4, Young's modulus is quite low compared with CVD-grown diamond and SiC films, with a Young's modulus as high as three times. Higher stiffness materials are more desirable, because the internal stresses of the absorbers, which can distort mask patterns, are less of an issue. Unfortunately, diamond and SiC membranes are also the most difficult to produce.

Table 2. Comparison of Membrane Materials for X-Ray Masks

Material	X-ray transparency	Observations
Silicon	0 (50% transmission at 5.5 μ m thickness).	Single-crystal Silicon, stacking faults cause scattering to occur, material is brittle. Amorphous with resistance to fracture.
SiC	0 (50% transmission at 2.3 μ m thickness).	High stiffness and transparency
Diamond	0 (50% transmission at 4.6 μ m thickness).	

The requirements on the absorber are high attenuation (>10 dB), stability under radiation over an extended period of time, negligible distortion, ease of patterning, and low microstructural defect density. Typical absorber materials are listed in Table 3. Gold is used most commonly, tungsten and other materials are used infrequently. In the semiconductor industry, an absorber thickness of 0.5 μ m might be sufficient, whereas x-ray lithography deals with thicker layers of resist, requiring a thicker absorber material to maintain the same resolution.

Table 3. Comparison of Absorber Materials for X-Ray Masks

Material	Observations
Gold	Not the best stability (grain growth), low stress, electroplating only, defects repairable (thermal exp coefficient 14.2oC-1 10-6) (0.7 μ m for 10 dB).
Tungsten	Refractory and stable, special care is needed for stress control, dry etchable, repairable (thermal exp coefficient 4.5oC-1 10-6) (0.8 μ m for 10 dB).
Tantalum	Refractory and stable, special care is needed for stress control, dry etchable, repairable.
Alloys	Easier stress control, greater thickness needed to obtain 10 dB.

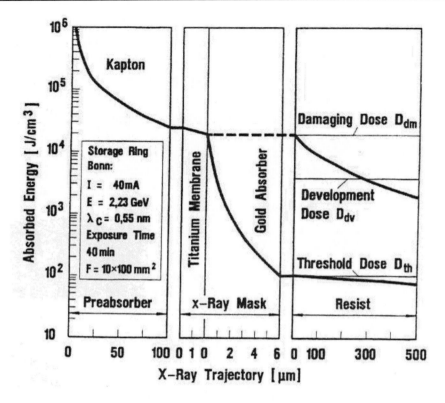

Figure 4. Absorbed energy along the x-ray trajectory including a 500 μ m thick PMMA specimen, x-ray mask, and a Kapton pre-absorber. After P. Bley, W. Menz, W. Bacher, K. Feit, M. Harmening, H. Hein, J. Mohr, W. Schomberg and K. Stark, "Application of the LiGA Process in the Fabrication of 3-D Structures", 4th International Symposium on Microprocess Conference, Japan, 1991, p.p. 384-389.

Figure 4 illustrates how x-rays, with a characteristic wavelength of 0.55 nm, are absorbed along their trajectory through a Kapton pre-absorber filter, an x-ray mask, and resist. The low-energy portion of the synchrotron radiation is absorbed mainly in the top portion of the resist layer, since absorption increases with increasing wavelength. The Kapton pre-absorber filters out much of the low-energy radiation to prevent over exposure of the top surface of the resist. The x-ray dose at which the resist gets damaged, Ddm, and the dose required for development of the resist, Ddv, as well as the "threshold dose" at which the resist starts dissolving in a developer, Dth, are all indicated in Figure 4. In the areas under the absorber pattern of the x-ray mask, the absorbed dose must stay below the threshold dose, Dth. Otherwise, the structures partly dissolve, resulting in poor feature definition. From Figure 4, we can deduce that the height of the gold absorbers must exceed 6 μ m to reduce the absorbed radiation dose of the resist under the gold pattern to below the threshold dose, Dth. In Figure 5, the necessary thickness of the gold absorber patterns of an x-ray mask is plotted as a function of the thickness of the resist to be patterned; the Au must be thicker for thicker resist layers and for shorter characteristic wavelengths, λc, of the x-ray radiation. To pattern a 500 mm high structure with a λc of 0.225 nm, the gold absorber must be more than 11 μ m in height.

Exposure of more extreme photoresist thicknesses requires x-ray photon energies that are significantly higher. At 3000 eV, the absorption length in PMMA roughly measures 100

$^{\mu}$ m, which enables the above-mentioned 500 $^{\mu}$ m exposure depth. Using 20,000 eV photons results in absorption lengths of approximately 1 cm. PMMA structures up to 10 cm thick have been exposed this way. A high-energy mask for high-energy exposures has a gold absorber 50 $^{\mu}$ m thick and a blank membrane of 400 $^{\mu}$ m thickness of silicon. An absorption contrast of 400 when exposing a 1000 $^{\mu}$ m thick PMMA sheet can be obtained. An advantage of using such thick silicon blank membranes is that larger resist areas can be exposed, since it does not depend on a fragile membrane-absorber combination.

4.4.3. Single-layer Absorber Fabrication

To make a mask with gold absorber structures of a height above 10 $^{\mu}$ m, one must first succeed in structuring a resist of that thickness. The height of the resist should be higher than the absorber itself so as to accommodate the electrodeposited metal in between the resist features. Currently, no means to structure a resist of that height with sufficient accuracy and perfect verticality of the walls exists, unless x-rays are used. Different procedures for producing x-ray masks with thicker absorber layers using a two-stage lithography process have been developed. The intermediate mask starts with a 3 $^{\mu}$ m thick resist layer, in which case the needed line-width accuracy and photoresist wall steepness of printed features are achievable. After gold plating in between the resist features and stripping of the resist, this intermediate mask is used to write a pattern with x-rays in a thicker resist, say 20 $^{\mu}$ m thick. After electrodepositing and resist stripping, the actual x-ray mask (that is, the master mask) is obtained.

Since hardly any accuracy is lost in the copying of the intermediate mask with x-rays to obtain the master mask, it is the intermediate mask quality that determines the ultimate quality of the x-ray lithographic-produced microstructures. The structuring of the resist in the intermediate mask is handled with optical techniques when the requirements of the x-ray lithography structures are less stringent. The minimal lateral dimensions for optical lithography in a 3 $^{\mu}$ m thick resist typically measure about 2.5 $^{\mu}$ m. Under optimal conditions, a wall angle of 88° is achievable. With e-beam lithography, a minimum lateral dimension of less than 1 $^{\mu}$ m is feasible. The most accurate pattern transfer is achieved through reactive ion etching of a tri-level resist system. In this approach, a 3 to 4 $^{\mu}$ m thick polyimide resist is first coated to the titanium or beryllium membrane, followed by a coat of 10 to 15 nm titanium deposited with magnetron sputtering. The thin layer of titanium is an excellent etch mask for the polyimide; in an optimized oxygen plasma, the titanium etches 300 times slower than the polyimide. To structure the thin titanium layer itself, a 0.1 $^{\mu}$ m thick optical resist is used. Since this top resist layer is so thin, excellent lateral tolerances result. The thin Ti layer is patterned with optical photolithography and etched in argon plasma. After etching the thin titanium layer, exposing the polyimide locally, the oxygen plasma helps to structure the polyimide down to the titanium or beryllium membrane. Lateral dimensions of 0.3 $^{\mu}$ m can be obtained in this fashion. Patterning the top resist layer with an e-beam increases the accuracy of the three-level resist method even further. Electrodeposition of gold on the titanium or beryllium membrane and stripping of the resist finishes the process of making the intermediate x-ray lithography mask. To make a master mask, this intermediate mask is printed by x-ray radiation onto a PMMA-resist-coated master mask. The PMMA thickness corresponds to a bit more than the desired absorber thickness. Since the resist layer thickness is in the 10 to 20 μ m range, a synchrotron x-ray wavelength of 0.1nm is adequate for the making of the master mask. A further improvement in x-ray lithography mask making is to fabricate intermediate and master mask on the same substrate, greatly reducing the risk for deviations in dimensions caused, for example, by temperature variations during printing.

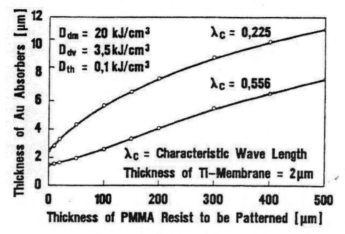

Figure 5. Minimum thickness of gold absorbers used for the x-ray mask. After P. Bley, W. Menz, W. Bacher, K. Feit, M. Harmening, H. Hein, J. Mohr, W. Schomberg and K. Stark, "Application of the LiGA Process in the Fabrication of 3-D Structures", 4th International Symposium on Microprocess Conference, Japan, 1991, p.p. 384-389.

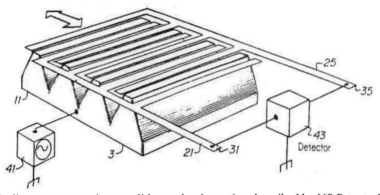

Figure 6. Mask alignment system in x-ray lithography. Invention described by US Patents 4,654,581 (Registered in 1987) and 4,607,213 (Registered in 1986).

4.4.4. Alignment of X-Ray Mask

The mask and resist-coated substrate must be properly registered to each other before they are placed in an x-ray scanner. Alignment of an x-ray mask to the substrate is a problem, since no visible light can pass through most x-ray membranes. To solve this problem windows are etched in a titanium x-ray membrane. Diamond membranes have a potential advantage here, as they are optically transparent and enable easy alignment for multiple irradiations without a need for etched holes.

Figure 6 illustrates an alternative, x-ray alignment system involving capacitive pickup between conductive metal fingers on the mask and ridges on a small substrate area; Si, in this case (US Patent 4,607,213 [Registered in 1986] and 4,654,581 [Registered in 1987]). When using multiple groups of ridges and fingers, two axis lateral and rotational alignment become possible. Another alternative may involve liquid nitrogen-cooled Si (Li) x-ray diodes as alignment detectors, eliminating the need for observation with visible light.

4.4.5. Masks for High-Aspect-Ratio Microlithography

A procedure has been developed to eliminate the need for an x-ray mask membrane. Unlike conventional masks, the so-called x-ray transfer mask does not treat a mask as an independent unit. The technique is based on forming an absorber pattern directly on the resist surface forming a conformal, self-aligned, or transfer mask. An example process is shown in Figure 7. In this sequence, a transfer mask plating base is first prepared on the PMMA substrate plate by evaporating 0.7nm of chromium (as adhesion layer) followed by 50 nm of gold using an electron beam evaporator. A 3 μ m thick layer of standard Novolak-based resist is then applied over the plating base and exposed in contact mode through an optical mask using an ultraviolet exposure station. Three micrometers of electroplated gold on the exposed plating base further completes the transfer mask. A blanket exposure and subsequent development remove the remaining resist. The 50 nm of Au plating base is dissolved by a dip of 20 to 30 s in a solution of potassium iodide (5%) and iodine (1.25%) in water; the Cr adhesion layer is removed by a standard chromium etch.

Fabrication of the transfer mask can thus be performed using standard lithography equipment available at almost any lithography shop. Depending on the resolution required, the x-ray transfer mask can be fabricated using known photon, e-beam, or x-ray lithography techniques. The patterning of the PMMA resist with a self-aligned mask is accomplished in multiple steps of exposure and development. An example of a cylindrical resonator made this way is shown in Figure 8. Each exposure/development step involves an exposure dose of approximately 8 to 12 J/cm2. Subsequent 5-min development steps remove ~30 μ m of PMMA. In seven steps, a self-supporting 1.5 mm thick PMMA resist is patterned to a depth of more than 200 μ m. The resist pattern shown in Figure 8 is 230 μ m thick and exhibits a 2 μ m gap between the inner cylinder and the pickup electrodes (aspect ratio is 100:1). The resonator pattern was produced using soft (1 nm length) x-rays and a 3 μ m thick Au absorber only.

Forming of the transfer mask directly on the sample surface creates several additional new opportunities; besides in situ development, etching, and deposition, these include exposure of samples with curved surfaces and dynamic deformation of a sample surface during the exposure (hemispherical structures for lenses are possible this way). The authors summarize the advantages of the transfer mask method as follows:

- Alleviates the difficulty in fabricating fragile mask membranes;
- Avoids alignment requirements during successive exposure steps;
- Reduces exposure time and absorber thickness for the same exposure source;
- Enhances pattern transfer fidelity, since there is almost no proximity gap;

- Avoids thermal deformation caused by exposure heat;
- Increases photoresist development rate by step-wise elevated exposure dose.

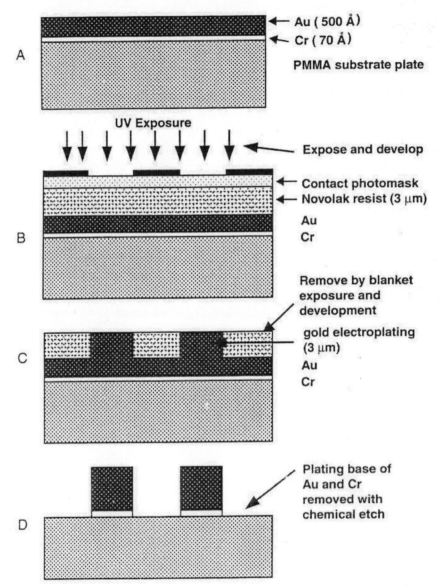

Figure 7. Sample transfer mask formation. (After M. Madou, 'Fundamentals of Microfabrication', 2nd Edition, 2002, CRC Press).

4.4.6. Choice of Resist Substrate

In the x-ray lithography process, the primary substrate, or base plate, must be a conductor or an insulator coated with a conductive top layer. A conductor is required for subsequent electrodeposition. Some examples of primary substrates that have been used successfully are Al, austenite steel plate, Si wafers with a thin Ti or Ag/Cr top layer, and copper plated with gold, titanium, or nickel. Other metal substrates as well as metal-plated ceramic, plastic, and glass plates have been employed. It is important that the plating base provide good adhesion for the resist. For that purpose, prior to applying the x-ray resist on copper or steel, the surface sometimes is mechanically roughened by micro grinding with corundum or other abrasive media.

Figure 8.(Continued).

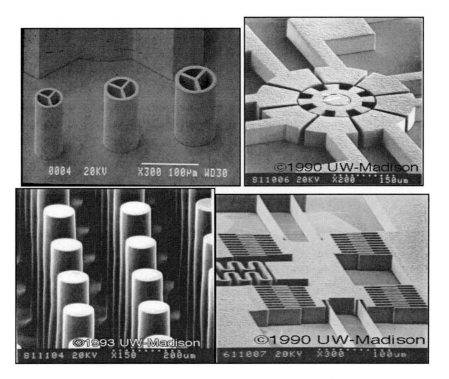

Figure 8. SEM micrographs of microstructures made by the transfer mask method and multiple exposure/development steps. Courtesy of Henry Guckel at the University of Wisconsin at Madison, US.

During chemical preconditioning, the titanium layer, sputter-deposited onto the polished metal base plate (e.g., Cu plate), is oxidized for a few minutes in a solution of 0.5 M NaOH and 0.2 M H_2O_2 at 65 OC. The oxide produced typically measures 30 nm thick and exhibits a micro rough surface instrumental to securing resist to the base plate. The Ti adhesion layer may further be covered with a thin nickel seed layer (~15 nm) for electroless or electroplating of nickel. When using a highly polished Si surface, adhesion promoters need to be added to the resist. A substrate of special interest is a processed silicon wafer with integrated circuits. Integrating the x-ray lithography process with semiconductor circuitry on the same wafer will create additional x-ray lithographic applications.

The rear surface of electrodeposited micro devices is attached to the primary substrate but can be removed from the substrate if required. In the latter case, the substrate may be treated chemically, or electrochemically, to intentionally induce poor adhesion. Ideally, excellent adhesion exists between substrate and resist, and poor adhesion exists between the electroplated structure and the plating base. Achieving these two contradictory demands is one of the main challenges in x-ray lithography.

4.4.7. Resist Requirements

An x-ray resist ideally should have high sensitivity to x-rays, high resolution, resistance to dry and wet etching, thermal stability of greater than 140OC, and a matrix or resin absorption of less than 0.35 μ m-1 at the wavelength of interest. These requirements are only those for semiconductor production with x-ray lithography. To produce high-aspect-ratio microstructures with high lateral tolerances an additional set of requirements is required. The unexposed resist must be absolutely insoluble during development. This means that a high contrast (γ) is required. The resist must also exhibit very good adhesion to the substrate and be compatible with the electroforming process. The latter imposes a resist glass transition temperature (Tg) greater than the temperature of the electrolyte bath used to electrodeposit metals between the resist features remaining after development (say, at 60 OC). To avoid mechanical damage to the microstructures induced by stress during development, the resist layers should exhibit low internal stresses. If the resist structure is the end product of the fabrication process, further specifications depend on the application itself, for example, optical transparency and refractive index for optical components or large mechanical yield strength for load-bearing applications. Owing to excellent contrast and good process stability known from e-beam lithography, PMMA is the preferred resist for deep-etch synchrotron radiation lithography. Two major concerns with PMMA as the x-ray lithography resist are a rather low lithographic sensitivity of about 2J/cm2 at a wavelength λc of 0.84 nm and a susceptibility to stress cracking. For example, even at shorter wavelengths, λc = 0.5 nm, over 90 min of irradiation are required to structure a 500 μ m thick resist layer with an average ring storage current of 40 mA and a power consumption of 2 MW at the 2.3-GeV ELSA synchrotron. The internal stress arising from the combination of a polymer and a metallic substrate can cause cracking in the microstructures during development, a phenomenon PMMA is especially prone to. X-ray resists explored for lithographic applications include poly(lactides), for example, poly(lactide-co-glycolide) (PLG); polymethacrylimide (PMI); polyoxymethylene (POM); and polyalkensulfone (PAS). PLG is a new positive resist that is more sensitive to x-rays by a factor of 2 to 3 compared with PMMA. From the comparison of different resists for deep x-ray lithography in Table 4, PLG emerges as the most promising x-ray lithography resist. POM, a promising mechanical material, may also be suited for medical applications given its biocompatibility. All of the resists shown in Table 4 exhibit significantly enhanced sensitivity compared to PMMA, and most exhibit reduced stress corrosion. Negative x-ray resists have inherently higher sensitivities compared to positive x-ray resists, although their resolution is limited by swelling. Poly(glycidyl methacrylate-co-ethyl acrylate) (PGMA), a negative e-beam resist has also been used in x-ray lithography. In general, resist materials sensitive to e-beam exposure also display sensitivity to x-rays and function in the same fashion; materials positive in tone for e-beam radiation typically are also positive in tone for x-ray radiation. A strong correlation exists between the resist sensitivities observed with these two radiation sources, suggesting that the reaction mechanisms might be similar for both types of irradiation. More common x-ray resists from the semiconductor industry are reviewed in Table 5.

4.4.8. Methods of Resist Application

Multiple Spin Coats

Different methods to apply ultra-thick layers of PMMA have been studied. In the case of multi-layer spin coating, high interfacial stresses between the layers can lead to extensive crack propagation upon developing the exposed resist.

Commercial PMMA Sheets

High molecular weight PMMA is commercially available as prefabricated plate and several groups have employed freestanding or bonded PMMA resist sheets for producing x-ray lithography structures. After overcoming the initial problems encountered when attempting to glue PMMA foils to a metallic base plate with adhesives, this has become the preferred method in several laboratories.

Table 4. Properties of Resists for Deep X-Ray Lithography

	PMMA	POM	PAS	PMI	PLG
Sensitivity	-	+	++	0	0
Resolution	++	0	--	+	++
Sidewall smoothness	++	--	--	+	++
Stress corrosion	-	++	+	-	+
Adhesion on substrate	+	+	+	-	+

Note: PMMA = poly(methylmethacrylate), POM = polyoxymethylene, PAS = Polyalkensulfone, PMI = polymethacrylimide, PLG = poly(lactide-co-glycolide). ++ = excellent; + = good; 0 = reasonable; - = bad; -- = very bad.

Casting of PMMA

PMMA also can be purchased in the form of a casting resin. In a typical procedure, PMMA is in situ polymerized from a solution of 35 wt% PMMA odf a mean molecular weight of anywhere from 100,000 g/-mol up to 106 g/mol in methylmethacrylate (MMA). Polymerization at room temperature takes place with benzoyl peroxide (BPO) catalyst as the hardener (radical builder) and dimethylaniline (DMA) as the initiator. The oxygen content in the resin, inhibiting polymerization, and gas bubbles, inducing mechanical defects, are reduced by degassing while mixing the components in a vacuum chamber at room temperature and at a pressure of 100 mbar for 2 to 3 min. In a practical application, resin is dispensed on a base plate provided with shims to define pattern and thickness and subsequently covered with a glass plate to avoid oxygen absorption.

Table 5. Resist materials used for E-Beam and X-Ray Lithography processes

Novolak-based resist	EBL sens (μC/cm2)	EBL Contrast	XRL sens (mJ/cm2)	XRL contrast
PMMA	100	2.0	6500	2.0
PBS	1	2.0	170	1.3
EBR-9	1.2	3.0		
Ray-PF			125	*
COP	0.5	0.8	100	1.1
GMCIA	7.0	1.7		
DCOPA			14	1.0
Novolak based	200-500	2-3	750-2000	~

* Indicates that the value is process dependent.

Resist Adhesion

Smooth surfaces such as Si wafers with an average roughness, Ra, smaller than 20 nm pose additional adhesion challenges that are often solved by modifying the resist itself. To promote adhesion of resist to polished untreated surfaces, such as a metal-coated Si wafers, coupling agents must be used to chemically attach the resist to the substrate. An example of such a coupling agent is methacryloxypropyl trimethoxy silane (MEMO). With 1 wt% of MEMO added to the casting resin, excellent adhesion results. The adherence is brought about by a siloxane bond between the silane and the hydrolyzed oxide layer of the metal. The integration of this coupling agent in the polymer matrix is achieved via the double bond of the methacryl group of MEMO. Hydroxyethyl methacrylate (HEMA) can improve PMMA adhesion to smooth surfaces, but higher concentrations are needed to obtain the same adhesion improvement. Silanization of polished surfaces prior to PMMA casting, instead of adding adhesion promoters to the resin, did not seem to improve the PMMA adhesion. In the case of PMMA sheets, as mentioned before, one option is solvent bonding of the layers to a substrate. In another approach, Galhotra et al. simply mechanically clamped the exposed and developed self-supporting PMMA sheet onto a 1.0 mm thick Ni sheet for subsequent Ni plating.

Stress-Induced Cracks in PMMA

The internal stress arising from the combination of a polymer on a metallic substrate can cause cracking in the microstructures during development. To reduce the number of stress-induced cracks, both the PMMA resist and the development process must be optimized. Detailed measurements of the heat of reaction, the thermomechanical properties, the residual monomer content, and the molecular weight distribution during polymerization and soft baking have shown the necessity to produce resist layers with a high molecular weight and with only a very small residual monomer content.

4.4.9. Exposure

Optimal Wavelength

For a given polymer, the lateral dimension variation in a x-ray lithography microstructure could, in principle, result from the combined influence of several mechanisms. These include Fresnel diffraction, the range of high-energy photoelectrons generated by the x-rays, the finite divergence of synchrotron radiation, and the time evolution of the resist profiles during the development process. The theoretical results demonstrate that the effect of Fresnel diffraction (edge diffraction), which increases as the wavelength increases, and the effect of secondary electrons in PMMA, which increases as the wavelength decreases, lead to minimal structural deviations when the characteristic wavelength ranges between 0.2 and 0.3 nm (assuming an ideal development process and no x-ray divergence). To fully utilize the accuracy potential of a 0.2 to 0.3nm wavelength, the local divergence of the synchrotron radiation at the sample site should be less than 0.1 mrad. Under these conditions, the variation in critical lateral dimensions likely to occur between the ends of a 500 $^\mu$ m high structure due to diffraction and secondary electrons is estimated to be 0.2 $^\mu$ m. The estimated Fresnel diffraction and secondary electron scattering effects are shown as a function of characteristic wavelength in Figure 9.

Using cross-linked PMMA, or linear PMMA with a unimodal and extremely high molecular weight distribution (peak molecular weight greater than 1,000,000 g/mol), the experimentally determined lateral tolerances on a test structure as shown in Figure 10 are 55 nm per 100 $^\mu$ m resist thickness, in good agreement with the 0.2 $^\mu$ m over 500 $^\mu$ m expected on a theoretical basis. These results are obtained only when a resist/developer system with a ratio of the dissolution rates in the exposed and unexposed areas of approximately 1000 is used. The use of resist layers, not cross-linked and displaying a relatively low bimodal molecular weight distribution, as well as the application of excessively strong solvents such as used to develop thin PMMA resist layers in the semiconductor industry, lead to more pronounced conical shape in the test structure of Figure 10. An illustration of the effect of molecular weight distribution on lateral geometric tolerances is that linear PMMA with a peak molecular weight below 300,000 g/mol shows structure tolerances of up to 0.15 $^\mu$ m/100 $^\mu$ m. To obtain the best tolerances requires a PMMA with a very high molecular weight, also a pre-requisite for low stress in the developed resist. Finally, if the synchrotron beam is not parallel to the absorber wall but at an angle greater than 50 mrad, greater angles may result.

4.4.10. Deposited Dose

The x-ray irradiation of PMMA reduces the average molecular weight. For one-component positive resists, this lowering of the average molecular weight causes the solubility of the resist in the developer to increase dramatically. The average molecular weight making dissolution possible is a sensitive function of the type of developer used and the development temperature. The molecular weight distribution, measured after resist exposure, is unimodal with peak molecular weights ranging from 3000 g/mol to 18,000 g/mol, dependent on the dose deposited during irradiation. The peak molecular weight increases nearly linearly with increasing resist depth; that is, decrease of the absorbed dose. Figure 11A illustrates a typical bimodal molecular weight distribution of PMMA before radiation, exhibiting an average molecular weight of 600,000. The gray region in this figure indicates the molecular weight region where PMMA readily dissolves; that is, below the 20,000-g/mol level for the temperature and developer used. Since the fraction of

PMMA with a 20,000 molecular weight is very small in nonirradiated PMMA, the developer hardly attacks the resist at all. After irradiation with a dose Ddv of 4 kJ/cm3, the average molecular weight becomes low enough to dissolve almost all of the resist (Figure 11B). With a dose Ddm of 20 kJ/cm3, all of the PMMA dissolves swiftly (Figure 11C). At a dose above Ddm, the microstructures are destroyed by the formation of bubbles. It follows that to dissolve PMMA completely and to make defect-free microstructures, the radiation dose for the specific type of PMMA used must lie between 4 and 20 kJ/cm3. These two numbers also lock in a maximum value of 5 for the ratio of the radiation dose at the top and bottom of a PMMA structure. To make this ratio as small as possible, the soft portion of the synchrotron radiation spectrum is usually filtered out by a pre-absorber (for example, a 100 $^\mu$ m thick polyimide foil [Kapton]) to reduce differences in dose deposition in the resist.

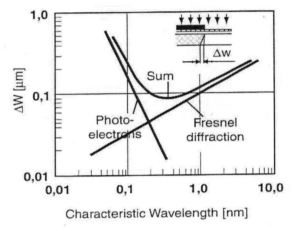

Figure 9. Fresnel diffraction and photoelectron generation as a function of characteristic wavelength, λc, and the resulting lateral dimension variation (Δ W). After W. Menz and P. Bley, "Microsystems for Engineers", VCH Publishers, Germany, 1993.

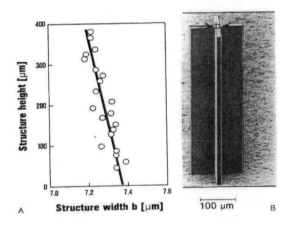

Figure 10. Structural tolerances. (A) SEM micrograph of a test structure to determine conical shape. (B) Structural dimensions as a function of structure height. The tolerances of the dimensions are within 0.2 $^\mu$ m over the total structure height of 400 $^\mu$ m. After J. Mohr, W. Ehrfeld, and D. Munchmeyer, in J. Vac. Sci. Technol., Volume B6, 1988, p.p. 2264-2267.

4.4.11. Stepped and Slanted Microstructures

For many applications, stepped or inclined resist sidewalls are very useful – consider, for instance, the fabrication of multi-level devices or prisms or, more basic yet, angled resist walls to facilitate the release of molded parts. Using stepped absorber layers on a single mask to make stepped multilevel microstructures are not always very well resolved. To make better-resolved stepped features, one can first relief print a PMMA layer, for example, by using a Ni mold insert made from a first x-ray mask. Subsequently, the relief structure may be exposed to synchrotron radiation to further pattern the polymer layer through a precisely adjusted second x-ray mask. To carry out this process, a two-layer resist system needs to be developed consisting of a top PMMA layer that fulfills the requirement of the relief printing process, and a bottom layer that fulfills the requirements of the x-ray lithography. The bottom resist layer promotes high molecular weight and adhesion, while the top PMMA layer is of lower molecular weight and contains an internal mold-release agent. This process sequence, combining plastic impression molding with x-ray lithography, is illustrated in Figure 12. The two-step resist then facilitates the fabrication of a mold insert by electroforming, which can be used for the molding of two-step plastic structures. Extremely large structural heights can be obtained from the additive nature of the individual microstructure levels. There are several options for achieving miniaturized features with slanted walls. It is possible to modulate the exposure/development times of the resist, fabricate an inclined absorber, angle the radiation, or, move the mask during exposure in so-called moving mask deep x-ray lithography.

To make a slanted absorber, a slab of material can be etched into a wedge by pulling it at a linear rate out of an etchant bath. Changing the angle at which synchrotron radiation is incident upon the resist, usually 90O, also enables the fabrication of microstructures with inclined sidewalls. This way, slanted microstructures may be produced by a single oblique irradiation or by a swivel irradiation. One potentially very important application of microstructures incorporating inclined sidewalls is the vertical coupling of light into waveguide structures using a 45O prism. Such optical devices must have a wall roughness of less than 50 nm, making x-ray lithography a preferred technique for this application. The sharp decrease of the dose in the resist underneath the edge of the inclined absorber, and the resulting sharp decrease of the dissolution of the resist as a function of the molecular weight in the developer, result in little or no deviation of the inclination of the resist sidewall over the total height of the microstructure.

4.4.12. Master Micromold Fabrication Methods

The high cost of x-ray lithography has required that engineers search for alternative means of fabricating high-aspect ratio metal or polymer micro masters. Micromold inserts (or micro masters) can be fabricated by a variety of alternate techniques such as CNC machining, silicon wet bulk micromachining, precision EDM, thick deep UV resists, DRIE, excimer layer ablation, and e-beam writing. In Table 6, x-ray lithography metal molds are compared with metal masters fabricated by other means. For example, comparing metal mold inserts made by spark erosive cutting and x-ray lithography, the latter proves far superior. X-ray lithographic PMMA features as small as 0.1 $^{\mu}$ m are replicated in the metal shape with almost no defects. The electroformed structures have a superior surface quality with a surface roughness, Ra, of less than 0.02 $^{\mu}$ m.

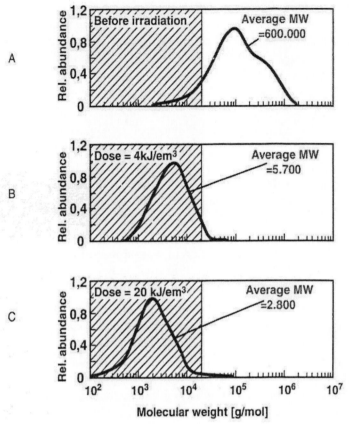

Figure 11. Molecular weight distribution of PMMA before (A) and after irradiation with 4 (B) to 20 kJ/cm3 (C). The shaded areas indicate the domain in which PMMA is minimally 50% dissolved. After W. Menz and P. Bley, "Microsystems for Engineers", VCH Publishers, Germany, 1993.

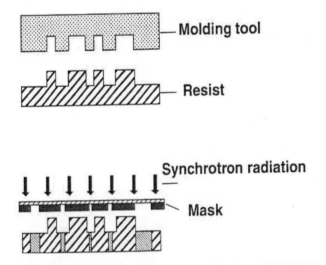

Figure 12. Stepped microstructures made in the x-ray lithography process. After W. Menz and P. Bley, "Microsystems for Engineers", VCH Publishers, Germany, 1993.

Table 6. Comparison of micromolds manufactured using a variety of techniques

Parameter	Laser	CNC Machining	Electro Discharge Machining	X-Ray Lithography	Deep Ultra Violet	Deep Reactive Ion Etching
Aspect Ratio	<10	14	<100	100	22	10-25
Roughness	100nm - 1^{μ} m	3-5 $^{\mu}$ m	0.3 - 1 $^{\mu}$ m	<20 nm	1^{μ} m	2^{μ} m
Accuracy	3-5 $^{\mu}$ m	3-5 $^{\mu}$ m	1-3 $^{\mu}$ m	<1 $^{\mu}$ m	2-3 $^{\mu}$ m	<1 $^{\mu}$ m
Maximum Height	300 $^{\mu}$ m	Unlimited	3-5 mm	<10mm	300 $^{\mu}$ m	300 $^{\mu}$ m
Mask Required?	No	No	No	Yes	Yes	Yes

DRIE and thick deep UV-sensitive resists such as polyimides, are recent contenders for micro master mold fabrication. With respect to dry etching, higher and higher aspect ratio features are being achieved; especially when using highly anisotropic etching conditions as in cryogenic DRIE. Wall roughness, causing form locking, remains a problem with DRIE; the dry etching process was optimized for speed, not for demolding. For small-quantity production, where the lifetime of mold inserts is not crucial, a silicon wafer etched by deep reactive-ion etching (DRIE) can be utilized directly as a mold insert for anywhere from 5 to 30 molding cycles.

For longer-lasting molds, metallizing the Si structure and using the metal as the mold is preferred. Photoresist structures on a silicon substrate have also been tested as a mold insert in plastic molding because of the simplicity and low cost of the process. In low-pressure molding processes, such mold inserts do work for a limited number of production processes (applying a thin metal layer over the top of the resist may further extend the lifetime of the mold), but their applicability in high-pressure processes needs to be further verified.

Both DUV and DRIE are more accessible than x-ray lithography and will continue to improve, taking more opportunities away from x-ray lithography. Like x-ray lithography, both alternative techniques can be coupled with plating, but neither technique can yet achieve the extreme low surface roughness and vertical walls of x-ray lithography. Other competing technologies for making metal masters are laser ablation methods and ultra-precision CNC machining. The latter three methods are serial processes and rather slow, but since we are considering the production of a master only, these technologies might well be competitive for certain applications.

Laser microablation produces minimum features of about 10 $^{\mu}$ m width and aspect ratios of 1:10. Challenges include taper and surface finish control. Recast layers around the laser drilled features cause form locking and infidelity in the replication. Femtosecond pulse layers promise thinner or even the absence of recast layers and excellent resolution. For large features (>50 $^{\mu}$ m) with tolerances and repeatability in the range of about 10 $^{\mu}$ m, traditional CNC-machining of materials like tool steel and stainless steel is often accurate enough for making metal mold inserts. The advantage of this technique is that the tool materials used are the same as those in conventional polymer molding, so their design, strength, and service life are well established. Complicated 3D structures can also be machined easily. The main disadvantages are that it is difficult to make sharp corners or right angles, and the surface quality is usually poor (surface roughness is around several μ m). In contrast, lithographic methods can produce molds with excellent surface quality (surface quality < 0.1 μ m) and sharp corners or right angles. However, they cannot be used on conventional tool materials like steel. Diamond-based micromilling and microdrilling reduce the surface roughness to 1 μ m or less. While diamond-based methods can achieve features smaller than 10 μ m, they are applicable only to "soft" metals such as nickel, aluminum, and copper.

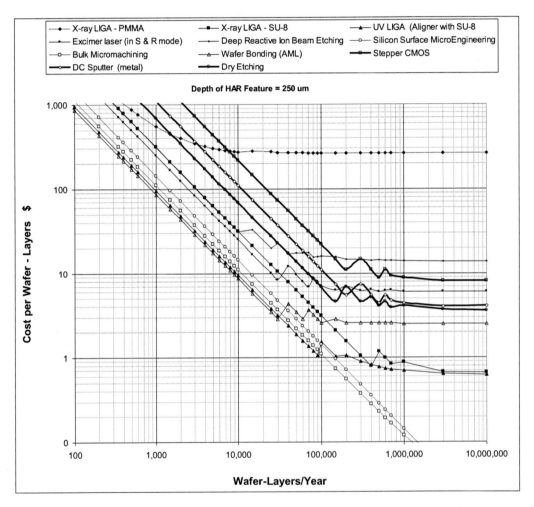

Figure 13. Cost per wafer for micromanufacturing and CMOS Processes as a function of wafer output (Inspired by Lawes, COMS 2007).

As shown in Table 6, a significant potential application of x-ray lithography remains the fabrication of those metal molds that cannot be accomplished with other techniques because of the tight wall roughness tolerances, small size, and high aspect ratios. From the table, it is obvious that x-ray lithography micromolds are extremely well suited at very low surface roughness levels and in terms of accuracy.

Summarizing, the requirements for an optimal mold insert fabrication technique are as follows:

- The master has to be removed from the molded structure, so the ease of release through wall inclination control is crucial;
- The most important parameters, including master life and achievable aspect ratios, depend very strongly on the surface quality of the master;
- The interface chemistry between master and polymer is a critical factor and must be controlled.

The costs associated with using different micromanufacturing processes has been analyzed by Lawes and was presented at COMS 2007 conference in St. Petersburg, Florida. Figure 13 shows the cost comparison of using different micromanufacturing processes for a high aspect ratio component. Figure 13 is used to make decisions on which process to select for manufacturing certain aspect ratio microcomponents.

5. CONCLUSIONS

The full potential of microfabrication using X-ray lithography and the LIGA technique has yet to be realised. Advances in process technology, a greater understanding of the physics of X-ray interactions in resist materials and the availability of more intense, higher energy beams from synchrotrons provide some solutions to earlier problems and new opportunities for industrial and commercial exploitation. The future value of the technique resides is its ability to mass-produce at low cost, precision micro components that cannot be made using other processes. This requires design rules and agreed standards in processing and manufacturing.

Most of the technical and process knowledge exists in research centers that have links or access to synchrotron sources. The limitation in the range of materials that can be electroformed preclude many application areas. This is however, offset by the growth in polymer and ceramic components required in almost all sectors of industry and, in particular medical diagnostics, chemical analysis, environmental sensors, optical displays and communications. The technology fits into the tool-making industry as basically precision molds and parts are used in the production process. The tool-making industry has an annual turnover of £45 billion and with a rapid growth rate predicted over the next five years it provides an ideal market sector for the technology.

Unfortunately there has been very little technology transfer into industry with only a few spin-off companies providing services and a limited number of products. In common with many non-IC based technologies, industry has not been convinced that LIGA has reached a level of maturity and a potential to mass-produce components that are free for defects and have total reliability. The high cost and accessibility to synchrotrons, the only suitable source of X-rays is one of the barriers to wider use of the technique. Germany saw future opportunities and in 1997 built and opened ANKA, 2.5 Gev Synchrotron facility with three dedicated lithography beam lines. It provides through a marketing subsidiary ANKA GmbH a full range of analytical and manufacturing services on a commercial basis.

Many countries in the Asia–Pacific rim are now looking at non-silicon based microfabrication technologies and have large growing markets for products. China, Taiwan, Korea, Singapore, have synchrotrons and microfabrication manufacturing facilities. They all are members of the global MEMS community and are adding to the research and development targeted towards the realization of commercial products. It is therefore likely that many of the problems mentioned above will be solved in the foreseeable future.

The recent establishment of an international LIGA Interest Group to bring together groups around the word and to act as a driver for commercialization is supported by Germany's FZK and the Sandia National Laboratories at Livermore, and the Centre for Advanced Microstructures and Devices (CAMD) at the Louisiana State University at Baton Rouge, in the US. This is a step towards making sure that all the work that has been carried out during the last sixteen years will be directed towards providing useful end-products.

REFERENCES

[1] Ehrfeld W, Becker E W, Hagmann P, Maner P and Munchmeyer P, Microelectron. *Engin.,* 1986, 4, 35-56.

[2] Bacher W et al IEE Transac. *Industrial Electron.,*42, (5), 1995.

[3] Hruby, J (Ed), Goettert , *J. Proceedings* HARMST 2003, Monterey, June 2003.

[4] Tolfree, D.W.L, *Proceedings of COMS2007,* Copenhagen, Denmark, Sept 2007.

[5] Goettert, *Proceedings of COMS2004,* Edmonton, Canada, Sept 2004.

[6] NEXUS *'Market Analysis for Microsystems* 2000-2005' Feb 2002.

[7] M. Madou, *'Fundamentals of Microfabrication'*, 2nd Edition, 2002, CRC Press).

[8] Tolfree, D.W L, Microfabrication using Synchrotron Radiation, *Progress Reports in Physics,* Vol61, No 4, 1998.

[9] Cerrina F *1996 Handbook on Lithography* SPIE editions.

[10] Becker E, Betz H, Ehrfeld W, Glashauser W, Michael H, Munchmeyer D, Pongratz S and Von Siemens R *1982 Naturwissenschaften* 69 520-523.

[11] Ehrfeld W, Becker E W, Hagmann P, Maner P and Munchmeyer P, *Microelectron. Engin.,* 1986 4 pp 35-56.

[12] Ehrfeld W, Bley P, Gotz F, Hagmann P, Mane A, Mohr J andHerbert O 1987 Proc IEEE Micro robots and Teleoperators Workshop (*Fabrication of Microstructures using the LIGA process)* 87 1-11.

[13] Ehrfeld W, Bley P, Gotz J, Munchmeyer D, Mohr J, Schulb W, 1988, *J Vac Sci* B6.

[14] Ehrfeld W and Lehr H 1994 Journal de Physique, Vol.4,p C9-229-236.

[15] Ehrfeld W and Lehr H 1995 *Rad. Phys & Chem* 45 pp349-365.

[16] Bley P, Gottert, Haemening M, Himmelhaus M, Menz W, Mohr J, Muller C and Wallrabe U 1991 *Microsystem Technologies 1991* (ed H Reichl), 302-314, Heidelberg, Springer-Verlag.

[17] Bley P 1993 Interdisciplinary Science Reviews Vol 18 No.3 p 267.

[18] Harmening M, Bacher W, Bley P, El-Kholi, Kalb H, Kowanz, Menz, *Michel A and Mohr J* 1992 MEMS No,0-7803-0497-7/92. 202-207, New York IEEE.

[19] Tolfree D and Ehrfeld W 1994 *Proc Tech Trans.*Conf, Pub by TCD.

[20] Bacher W, Menz W and Mohr J 1995 *IEE Trans. on Industrial Elect.* Vol 42.

[21]   Guckel H, Skrobis K, Christenson T, Klein J, Han, Choi B, Loverell E and Chapman T *1991 proc. Transducers* (San Francisco) (New York : IEEE).

[22]   Guckel H 1993 *N I M in Physics Res, section B* Vol B79 no 1-4 pp 247-8.

[23]   Guckel H, Skrobis K, Christenson T and Klein J 1994 *SPIE's Symposium on Microlithography* pp 2194-09.

[24]   Guckel H and Christenson T R 1995 *SPIE Meeting,* Oct. 1995, Austin, Texas.

[25]   Tomboulian D H and Hatman 1956 *Phys. Rev.* 102 1423-47.

[26]   Sokolov A A and Ternov I M 1957 *Sov. Phys. JETP* 4 396-400.

[27]   Sokolov A A and Ternov I M 1968 *Synchrotron Radiation* (Berlin : Academie-Verlag).

[28]   Godwin R P 1969 Synchrotron Radiation as a Light Source (*Springer Tracts in Modern Physics* 51, ed. Hohler.

[29]   Rowe E M 1979 *Synchrotron Radiation* (topics in Current Physics 10) ed C Kunz (Berlin Springer) pp 25-54.

[30]   Winick H 1980 *Synchroton Radiation Research ed Winick and Doniach (*New York: Plenum) pp11-60.

[31]   Grobman W 1985 *Synchrotron Radiation Research Winick* H ed. Pergamon NY.

[32]   Ternov I M, Mikhailin V V and Khalilov V R 1985 *Synchrotron Radiation and its Applications* (New York: Harwood).

[33]   Marks N 1995 Radiat. *Phys, Chem.* Vol 45, No. 3, pp 315-331.

[34]   Turner S 1989, Synchrotron Radiation and Free Electron Lasers*, CERN Acc. School, Chester, Cern* 90-30.

[35]   Krinsky S, Perlman M L and Watson R E 1993 Handbook on Synchrotron Radiation E Koch ed. *North Holland* pp. 65-172.

[36]   Tomboulian D H and Hatman 1956 *Phys. Rev.* 102 1423-47.

[37]   Timothy J G and Madden R P 1983 *Handbook on Synchrotron Radiation* Vol 1A, ed E E Koch (Amersterdam : North-Holland) pp325-66.

[38]   Elleaume P 1990 *Phys. Scripta* T31 67-71.

[39]   Yamamonto S, Shio T, Sasaki S and Kitamura H, 1989*, Rev Sci. Instrum.,* 60, 1834-7.

In: Micro and Nanomanufacturing Research   ISBN 978-1-61942-003-8
Editor: J. Paulo Davim   © 2012 Nova Science Publishers, Inc.

Chapter 2

MECHANISTIC MODELING APPROACH FOR MICRO MILLING CUTTING FORCES

Mohammad Malekian, Simon S. Park,

Micro Engineering Dynamics Automation Laboratory, Department of Mechanical and
Manufacturing Engineering, University of Calgary, 2500 University Dr. NW, Calgary,
Alberta, Canada T2N 1N4, Canada

Martin B. G. Jun[*]

Laboratory for Advanced Multi-scale Manufacturing
Department of Mechanical Engineering, University of Victoria
PO Box 3055 STN CSC, Victoria, British Columbia, Canada V8W 3P6, Canada

ABSTRACT

In this chapter, the chip thickness model that considers the elastic-plastic nature of
the ploughing/rubbing and elastic recovery is first summarized, followed by development
of the mechanistic micro milling force models separately developed for the ploughing
and shearing dominant regimes. Then, estimation methods for specific cutting energies
and the model parameters is presented, followed by summary of experimental validation
results using the mechanistic model.

NOMENCLATURE

A_p	ploughed area $[mm^2]$
e	error
f_t	feed rate $[mm/flute]$
F_t	tangential force $[N]$

[*] Corresponding author, E-mail: mbgjun@uvic.ca

F_r	radial force $[N]$
F_{exp}	experimental force $[N]$
F_{theo}	theoretical force $[N]$
h	chip thickness $[mm]$
h_c	minimum chip thickness $[mm]$
h_{er}	height of elastic recovery $[mm]$
K_{rc}, K_{tc}	radial and tangential cutting coefficients $[N/mm^2]$
K_{re}, K_{te}	radial and tangential edge coefficients $[N/mm]$
K_{rp}, K_{tp}	radial and tangential ploughing coefficients $[N/mm^3]$
N	number of flutes
p_e	elastic recovery $[\%]$
r_e	edge radius $[mm]$
r_o	tool run-out $[mm]$
V_p	ploughed volume $[mm^3]$
X_c, Y_c	location of the tool centre $[mm]$
Δ	rpm of the spindle $[rev/min]$
θ	immersion angle $[rad]$
ψ_e	clearance angle $[rad]$
ψ_b, ψ_s	geometric angles $[rad]$

1. INTRODUCTION

Highly accurate miniaturized components that are made up of a variety of engineering materials play key roles in the future development of a broad spectrum of products [1]. Many innovative products require higher functionality with significantly decreased size; however, conventional fabrication methods using photolithographic fabrication methods are not applicable to all engineering materials, and the processes are slow and expensive and limited to essentially planar geometries [2]. To overcome the challenges, micro mechanical machining processes can be utilized to remove materials mechanically using a miniature tool to create complex three- dimensional shapes using a variety of engineering materials [3, 4]. Micro mechanical machining techniques bring many advantages to the fabrication of micro-sized features. They can produce micro components cost-effectively because there is no need for expensive photolithographic masks. The flexibility and efficiency of micro machining processes using miniature cutting tools allows for the economical fabrication of smaller batch sizes compared with other processes [5].

Due to the miniature nature of the mechanical removal process, micro machining operations are susceptible to excessive tool wear, noise, and poor productivity. Thus, the modeling and understanding of micro cutting processes are important to improve the machined part quality and increase productivity. The mechanistic approach for cutting force modeling has been very effective for parameter estimation, process monitoring and control, and understanding of the process. However, the conventional mechanistic modeling approach cannot be applied to micro-scale cutting. In micro milling operations, the cutting edge radius of the end mill is comparable in size to the chip thickness [6]. As a result, no chip is formed when the chip thickness is below the minimum chip thickness [7, 8]; instead, part of the work material plastically deforms under the edge of the tool, and the rest elastically recovers. This change in the chip formation process, known as the minimum chip thickness effect and the associated material elastic recovery, causes increased cutting forces [9] and surface roughness [10] at low feed rates.

When the chip actually forms during a micro milling operation with a finite edge radius tool, ploughing under the edge contributes to an increase in the specific energy or cutting coefficients. The key aspect of the mechanistic modeling approach is the specific cutting energies, which have been observed to increase as the uncut chip thickness is decreased, a phenomenon commonly known as the size effect. Many researchers have investigated the effect of ploughing on the size effect. Armarego and Brown [11] suggested that the greater relative contribution of the ploughing forces with a blunt tool is responsible for the increase in the specific cutting energy. Similarly, Lucca et al. [12] showed that the ploughing and elastic recovery, which were used to explain the increase in the cutting force, of the workpiece along the flank face of the tool play a significant role in micro machining. Komanduri [13] studied the ploughing mechanism experimentally by using sharp tools with extremely negative rake angles to replace the rounded-edge tools.

In order to understand the ploughing mechanisms, ploughing force models have been developed by many researchers. Vogler et al. [9] made the first attempt at incorporating the effect of minimum chip thickness into a micro end milling force model. They used the slip-line plasticity model developed by Waldorf et al. [14]. More complicated slip-line plasticity models that account for elastic-plastic deformation and elastic recovery have been developed by Jun et al. [15]. Fang also developed a universal slip-line model for rounded-edge tools [16]. The finite element model approach has also been utilized by many researchers to model the micro cutting process and to understand size effect [17], machining stresses [18, 19], and the influence of cutting edge radius on wear resistance [20]. However, the majority of these methods require many assumptions, and the parameters used in the model are difficult to estimate. There are a few mechanistic models developed for micro end milling processes [21-24], but these models do not consider the effects of edge radius, minimum chip thickness, and elastic recovery. Recently, a new mechanistic micro end milling force model has been developed with consideration of the aforementioned effects [25]. It has been observed to be very effective in predicting micro milling forces both in ploughing and shearing regimes.

2. MECHANISTIC CUTTING FORCE MODEL

2.1. Chip Thickness Modeling

In micro machining, the edge radius of the tools is considerably large compared to the uncut chip thickness; as a result, the so-called minimum chip thickness phenomenon occurs in micro machining. Thus, when the uncut chip thickness is less than the minimum chip thickness (h_c), no chip formation occurs and only ploughing/rubbing takes place. Material separation occurs when the uncut chip thickness is greater than the critical minimum chip thickness (h_c), or at what is sometimes referred to as the stagnation point [26, 27], when the material above the minimum chip thickness forms a chip and the material below the minimum chip thickness deforms under the edge with a partial elastic recovery, resulting in material ploughing.

Consider a discretized axial slice an end mill in the axial direction with a helix angle of 30° as shown in Figure 1. It shows the ploughing process at the ith rotational angle in micro end milling, when the chip thickness is less than the minimum chip thickness for an arbitrary axial slice, where θ_i represents the angles at the ith rotational angle, h is the uncut chip thickness, h_{er} is the height of elastic recovery, r_e is the edge radius, ψ_e is the clearance angle, and A_p is the ploughed area (represented by the hatched area) at the rotational angle. The shaded area represents the ploughed material. The ploughed volume, V_p, at the rotational angle, θ_i, can be obtained by summing up the ploughed areas (A_p) of all the axial slices along the cutting edge.

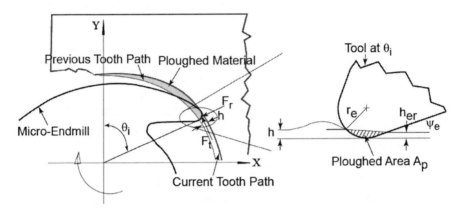

Figure 1. Ploughing due to finite edge radius in micro-end milling.

When the chip thickness, h, increases to greater than the minimum chip thickness, h_c, the ploughing becomes negligible, and the elastic recovery drops to zero (Figure 5). Thus, in micro end milling, each flute goes through different material removal mechanisms in a single path, and the cutting mechanisms switch back and forth from the ploughing dominant regime to the shearing dominant regime [27], depending on the uncut chip thickness value, as shown in Figure 2.

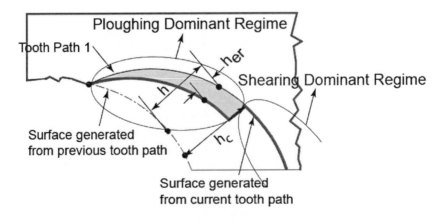

Figure 2. Chip thickness in the ploughing dominant regime.

A comprehensive chip thickness model was developed in [15] to compute the correct chip thickness, including the effects of the trochoidal tool path, minimum chip thickness, elastic recovery, and tool vibrations. Figure 3 shows the surface generation and chip thickness computation in the presence of elastic recovery, which is represented as the shaded region, for an arbitrary axial slice. Points C and F represent the tool centre and cutting edge locations, respectively. The superscript denotes the tooth pass number, and the subscript represents the rotational angle. Point I is found at the intersection between the previously generated surface from the previous tooth pass and the line connecting C and F for the current tooth pass. The chip thickness can be formulated as [15]:

$$h = \max\left(0, \left\|C_i^j F_i^j\right\| - \left\|C_i^j I_i^{j-1}\right\|\right). \tag{1}$$

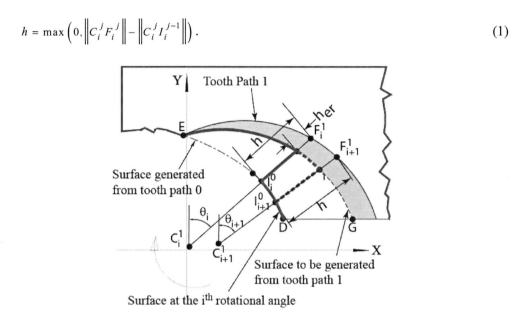

Figure 3. Chip thickness model considering elastic recovery [15].

2.2. Force Model Development in the Ploughing Dominant Regime

Chip formation does not occur when the uncut chip thickness is less than the minimum chip thickness; instead, there is ploughing and partial elastic recovery of the material. For mechanistic modeling for the ploughing forces, they are modeled as proportional to the volume of interference between the tool and the workpiece. Many researchers have employed this procedure in the modeling of the forces due to interference between the clearance face of the tool and the workpiece for orthogonal cutting [28, 29], turning [30, 31], and micro end milling processes [9]. However, none of these modeling approaches have considered the effect of the elastic recovery during the ploughing process, as full elastic recovery was assumed for all materials. It has been shown that the effect of the elastic recovery on the micro end milling process is substantial [32]. Thus, it is important to model the ploughing forces as proportional to the volume of interference between the tool and the workpiece, considering the effect of the elastic recovery [25].

Figure 4 shows two different cases: the height of elastic recovery (h_{er}) is greater than or equal to $r_e(1-\cos\psi_e)$, i.e. $h_{er} \geq r_e(1-\cos\psi_e)$; and the height of elastic recovery (h_{er}) is less than $r_e(1-\cos\psi_e)$, i.e. $h_{er} < r_e(1-\cos\psi_e)$ [25]. The elastic recovery height can be expressed as $h_{er} = p_e h$, where p_e is the elastic recovery rate. The shaded area represents the ploughed area for both cases. Angle α_p is the angle that the point on the rounded edge at the minimum chip thickness makes with respect to the y-axis, and it is given by:

$$\alpha_p = \cos^{-1}\left(1 - \frac{h}{r_e}\right) \tag{2}$$

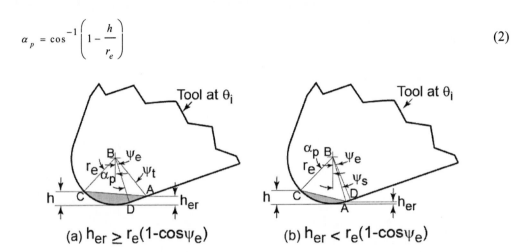

(a) $h_{er} \geq r_e(1-\cos\psi_e)$ 　　　　 (b) $h_{er} < r_e(1-\cos\psi_e)$

Figure 4. Ploughing area for two different cases: (a) $h_{er} \geq r_e(1-\cos\psi_e)$ and (b) $h_{er} < r_e(1-\cos\psi_e)$.

For both cases, point B represents the centre of the circle or the rounded edge, and point D the end of the arc. Line l_{BD} is at the same angle as the clearance angle from the vertical line. Point A is at the height of the elastic recovery.

When $h_{er} \geq r_e(1-\cos\psi_e)$, the ploughed area, A_p, indicated by the shaded area in Figure 12(a), can be obtained as:

$$A_p = A_{BCD} + A_{ABD} - A_{ABC} \tag{3}$$

where A_{BCD} is the area of the arc segment, and A_{ABD} and A_{ABC} are the areas of the triangles connecting the corresponding points. Area A_{BCD} can be obtained by:

$$A_{BCD} \approx \frac{1}{2}r_e^2(\alpha_p + \psi_e) \tag{4}$$

The area A_{ABD} is given by:

$$A_{ABD} = \frac{r_e}{2}\left(\frac{h_{er} - r_e(1 - \cos\psi_e)}{\sin\psi_e}\right) = \frac{1}{2}r_e l_{AD} \quad \text{where}$$

$$l_{AD} = \left(\frac{h_{er} - r_e(1 - \cos\psi_e)}{\sin\psi_e}\right) \tag{5}$$

The area A_{ABC} can be obtained by:

$$A_{ABC} = \frac{1}{2} r_e l_{AB} \sin(\alpha_p + \psi_e + \psi_t) \tag{6}$$

where

$$l_{AB} = \sqrt{r_e^2 + l_{AD}^2}$$
$$\psi_t = \tan^{-1}\left(\frac{l_{AD}}{r_e}\right). \tag{7}$$

Thus, the ploughed area A_p can be expressed as:

$$A_p = \frac{1}{2} r_e^2 (\alpha_p + \psi_e) + \frac{1}{2} r_e l_{AD} - \frac{1}{2} r_e l_{AB} \sin(\alpha_p + \psi_e + \psi_t) \tag{8}$$

When $h_{er} < r_e(1 - \cos\psi_e)$, the ploughed area, A_p, indicated by the shaded area in Figure 12(b), can be obtained by:

$$A_p = \frac{1}{2} r_e^2 \left(\alpha_p + \psi_s - \sin(\alpha_p + \psi_s)\right) \tag{9}$$

where

$$\psi_s = \cos^{-1}\left(1 - \frac{h_{er}}{r_e}\right) \tag{10}$$

For a discretized disk element of a micro end mill flute, the ploughing volume can be expressed as $V_p = A_p dz$, where dz is the thickness of the disk element. Since the ploughing forces can be modeled as proportional to the volume of interference between the tool and the workpiece, both radial and tangential ploughing forces can be written as a multiplication of a constant and the ploughed volume. Therefore, the ploughing forces for each differential flute element can be computed as:

$$dF_{rp} = (K_{rp} A_p + K_{re}) dz$$
$$dF_{tp} = (K_{tp} A_p + K_{te}) dz \tag{11}$$

where K_{rp} and K_{tp} are the radial and tangential ploughing coefficients, respectively, and A_p can be determined from Equation 8 or 9. The unit for the ploughing coefficients is N/mm^3. The edge components, K_{re} and K_{te}, are the radial and tangential edge coefficients, respectively, and they represent friction between the tool and the workpiece. Since the edge coefficients represent friction as the uncut chip thickness goes to zero, the edge components in the ploughing dominant regime must be the same as those in the shearing dominant regime. Thus, the edge coefficients can be determined from experimental calibration of the coefficients in the shearing dominant regime. The ploughing coefficients are determined from experimental calibration in the ploughing dominant regime.

2.3. Force Model Development in the Shearing Dominant Regime

When the chip thickness is bigger than the critical value, the cutting mechanism is assumed to be similar to the conventional cutting mechanism that considers the shearing and edge coefficients. In milling operations, the tangential (dF_{ts}) and radial (dF_{rs}) shearing cutting forces acting on a differential flute element with height dz, as shown in Figure 1, can be modeled as follows, when the uncut chip thickness is greater than the minimum chip thickness value ($h>h_c$) [33]:

$$dF_{rs} = [K_{rc}h(\theta_i(z)) + K_{re}]dz$$
$$dF_{ts} = [K_{tc}h(\theta_i(z)) + K_{te}]dz$$

(12)

where dz is the height of the differential flute element; K_{rc} and K_{tc} are the radial and tangential cutting coefficients, respectively. The cutting coefficients represent shearing of the workpiece, and the edge components represent friction between the tool and the workpiece.

Therefore, the radial and tangential forces acting on a discretized disk element can now be expressed as:

$$dF_t = \begin{cases} (K_{tc}h + K_{te})dz & when \quad h \geq h_c \text{ (shearing)} \\ (K_{tp}A_p + K_{te})dz & when \quad h < h_c \text{ (ploughing)} \end{cases}$$

$$dF_r = \begin{cases} (K_{rc}h + K_{re})dz & when \quad h \geq h_c \text{ (shearing)} \\ (K_{rp}A_p + K_{re})dz & when \quad h < h_c \text{ (ploughing)} \end{cases}$$

(13)

where h = f(ft, θ, her, dx, dy, ro), Ap = f(h, re, her), ft is the feed per tooth, and θ is the rotational angle of the tool. The computed forces are summed among all the engaged axial slices over all the cutting flutes to obtain the total tangential and radial forces, which are then transformed to forces in the planar directions, with respect to the global coordinate system. This model suggests cutting and ploughing coefficients that inherently contain different aspects of plastic deformation, such as strain hardening and strain gradient effects. The friction forces are considered constant for different conditions and modeled with the edge coefficients.

Micro tools are very small in diameter; therefore, the tool deflection can be very significant during the cutting operations. This can result in excessive tool vibration and cutting forces, and poor surface quality. In order to accurately model the micro machining operations, it is important to predict the deflection of the tool subjected to the cutting forces. In conventional machining, this can be done by accurate measurement of the dynamics, i.e. the frequency response function (FRF) at the tool tip, using an instrumented hammer and a displacement sensor. However, since the diameter of micro end mills is very small and the tools are fragile, impact hammer testing cannot be applied directly to determine the dynamics of the tool tip. Therefore, receptance coupling (RC) of the spindle/machining centre and the micro tools can be employed to extract the dynamics at the tool tip [34. 35]. For simulation of micro milling cutting forces using Equation 13, the dynamics of the tool obtained from the RC coupling method was also simulated to obtain dynamic milling forces.

3. EXPERIMENTAL SETUP

In order to verify the mechanistic model in Equation 19, experiments have been conducted to determine the cutting, ploughing, and edge coefficients, and validate the model [25]. For these experiments, an ultra precision vertical CNC milling machine (Kern Micro 2255) with a spindle that can rotate from 60,000 to 160,000 rev/min (rpm) was used. The base of the machine is polymer concrete, which damps out external vibrations. Unlike many micro CNC systems, the CNC machine used in this study utilizes hybrid ball bearings, which provide higher stiffness and linearity, and an elaborate lubrication system that allows for temperature stability during the high-speed rotations. The accuracy of the stage is 1 micrometer. The experimental setup for this study is depicted in Figure 5.

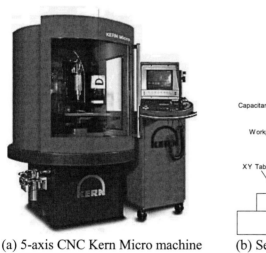
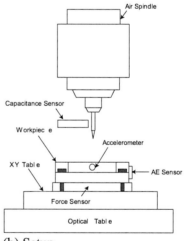

(a) 5-axis CNC Kern Micro machine   (b) Setup

Figure 5. Experimental Setup.

The micro tools used were tungsten carbide (WC) micro end mills with 500 µm diameter flat micro end mills (PMT TS-2-0200-S) with the clearance angle of approximately 10 degs. The tool overhang length was 15 mm from the collet; and, this value remained constant in order not to change the dynamics during the experiments. The scanning electron microscopy (SEM) picture of the tip of the 500 µm diameter carbide end mill is shown in Figure 6.

A piezoelectric table dynamometer (Kistler 9256C2) with an accuracy of 0.002 N was used to measure the micro cutting forces. The charge signals generated from the force sensor were fed into the charge amplifiers (Kistler 9025B), which converted the charge signals into voltage signals. The calibration of the table dynamometer was performed using both modal impact hammer tests (Dytran 5800SL) and a force gauge (Omega DFG51-2) to verify the force measurement. The sensitivity of the dynamometer was 26 pC/N for X and Y directions. The noise level was approximately 0.005 N which was insignificant compared to the cutting forces. The frequency bandwidth of the dynamometer was found to be approximately 1500 Hz from the impact hammer tests.

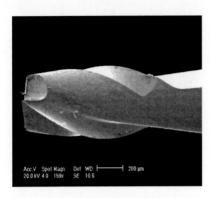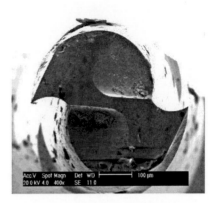

Figure 6. SEM pictures of the tool.

The zero point in the Z direction was found by moving the rotating tool down very slowly and looking at the acoustic emission (AE) signal carefully. As soon as the tool touched the workpiece, a sudden jump in the AE signal was observed, and the position was set to zero. The forces were preprocessed by subtracting air cutting forces from the measured cutting forces through synchronization at each revolution of the spindle using capacitance sensors (Lion Precision C3-D, RD20-2) with an accuracy of 10 nanometers. The measured force signals while the spindle was rotating without material removal (i.e. air cutting) were subtracted from the cutting forces during the material removal after synchronizing the two signals based on the capacitance sensor measurements. An AE sensor (Physical Acoustics Nano30) was used for capturing high-frequency vibrations. The accelerometers (Kistler 8778A500) were attached to the workpiece to measure vibration signals in both the X and Y directions. The workpiece material was Al6061-T6 with a hardness of 95 HB. The workpiece was attached with the aid of Mitee-Grip™ to a plate that could interface with the dynamometer.

4. CALIBRATION AND PARAMETER ESTIMATION

In order to come up with the micro cutting force model, the identification of specific energies or cutting coefficients is imperative. These coefficients can be obtained from the experimental data; therefore the accurate measurement of the cutting forces is important. Since the frequency bandwidth of the table dynamometer is typically not sufficient for high speed cutting operations (i.e. 1500 Hz) associated in micro milling, the measured cutting forces are need to be compensated for the unwanted dynamics of the table dynamometer. A Kalman filter method as outlined in [36] can be employed to accurately measure the high speed cutting forces based on the dynamics of the sensor.

Figure 7 shows the root mean square (RMS) value of the resultant force versus feed rate. As can be observed, for feed rates larger than approximately 2.5 µm/flute, the force has a linear trend. A linear curve fit of the forces in this region is also shown in this figure. In the ploughing dominant regime, the forces have increased values and vary smoothly, but do not follow the same linear behaviour and are bigger than the predicted values by the extrapolated linear curve fit (dashed line in Figure 9). A transition region between the ploughing and shearing regions has been defined, in which the forces do not follow a smooth curve. The force data in the shearing dominant regime can be used to obtain the cutting and edge coefficients. Since the micro end mills generally have two flutes, the average of the forces is nearly zero, and the ordinary method [35] of finding the coefficient does not work. Therefore, the cutting coefficients can be found via a nonlinear curve fitting. For this purpose, the following error is minimized through a steepest descent algorithm [37]:

$$e = \sum_{i=1}^{n} \sum_{j=1}^{m} (F_{\exp_{i,j}} - F_{theo})^2 \qquad (14)$$

where n is the number of feed rates considered in the shearing dominant region, m is the number of samples, F_{exp} is the instantaneous experimental forces data (stars in Figure 5), and F_{theo} is the theoretical force obtained from the conventional sharp-edge theorem using arbitrary initial values for the unknown coefficients. Full immersion cutting data were used for this purpose, since they showed better agreement with the theoretical data. To obtain the shearing dominant cutting coefficients, 8 different feed rates (n) with 500 samples (m) for each feed rate were used. Experimental and theoretical forces were synchronized before the optimization. The coefficients that minimized the error in Equation 14 are shown in Table 1.

As can be observed in Table 1, the cutting coefficients were bigger than those of the conventional end mills, which can be a result of round edges making the effective rake angle smaller or even negative, whereas the edge coefficients for the micro end mills were much less. This is perhaps due to the smaller contact area between the tool and the workpiece compared with macro milling operations.

When the uncut chip thickness is smaller than the critical value, an elastic recovery occurs that can affect the chip formation, cutting forces, and surface generation during machining operations. The elastic recovery is different for various materials and should be identified in order to accurately model the micro machining operations. It has been shown [38] that the elastic recovery rate of the material can be identified directly using instrumented conical scratch tests. In this method, the remaining grooves from the scratch tests are inspected using a surface profilometer. The surface profile of the groove can be measured with the aid of the profilometer, as shown in Figure 8. The area of the groove under the original surface ('abc' in Figure 13) is then calculated. Knowing this area and the projected area of the tool in the vertical direction ('ABC' in Figure 13), the elastic recovery rate of the material is acquired from:

The scratch tests were performed utilizing conical tools with an apex angle of 90°. The nominal depths of the grooves were chosen to be 5, 10 and 15 µm; and, the surface profile was measured at 3 different points for each groove. It was found that the average elastic recovery, p_e, of Aluminum 6061 was approximately 10 percent. This acquired elastic recovery was used as one of the parameters of the developed model for micro machining.

In order to obtain the ploughing coefficients in Equation 13, the same method used for the identification of the coefficients in the shearing dominant regime was utilized. The experimental and theoretical forces were synchronized for full immersion, and the defined error between the forces (Equation 14) was minimized for 10 different feed rates and 500 samples for each feed rate through the steepest descent method. To assure that the global minimum was obtained, the initial values of the parameters were varied several times. As a result, the ploughing coefficients were identified as shown in Table 2.

Table 1. The cutting constants for shearing dominant regime

Coefficients	K_{tc} (N/mm2)	K_{rc} (N/mm2)	K_{te} (N/mm)	K_{re} (N/mm)
Al 6061	3780	2300	1.05	0.81

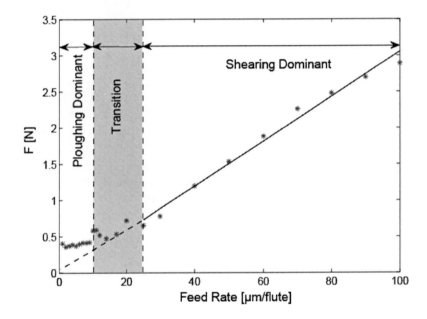

Figure 7. Micro milling resultant forces versus feed rate (full immersion, depth of cut of 100 μm).

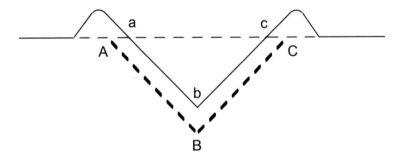

Figure 8. Finding elastic recovery through an indentation test using a conical indenter.

Table 2. The cutting constants and estimated parameter values for ploughing dominant regime

Coefficients	K_{tp} (KN/mm3)	K_{rp} (KN/mm3)	Runout (μm)	h_c (μm)	p_e
Al6061	1150	760	0.2	0.7	0.1

$$p_e = \frac{S_{ABC} - S_{abc}}{S_{ABC}}$$

$\qquad\qquad\qquad\qquad\qquad\qquad\qquad\qquad\qquad\qquad\qquad\qquad$ (15)

5. MODEL VALIDATION

Figure 9 shows the experimental and theoretical forces obtained using the identified coefficients for the feed rate of 9 μm/flute and the full immersion cutting condition in X and Y directions based on Equation 12 with the run-out. It can be seen that the conventional cutting theory with the coefficients shown in Table 1 can predict the forces in the shearing dominant regime properly and with good accuracy. Also, the forces for the feed rate of 9 μm/flute and the half immersion cutting condition are shown in Figure 10. Although the agreement between the experiments and simulations was not as good as what was observed for full immersion, there was still a good match between the data. The frequency content of the forces also shows good agreement between the experiments and the simulation

Figure 11 shows the experimental and theoretical forces obtained using the ploughing dominant formulation and the identified coefficients in Tables 1 and 2. It can be observed that there is good agreement between the simulation and the experiment, and the proposed model can properly model the more complex force profiles in the ploughing dominant regime. Also, the comparison between the simulations and the experimental data for half immersion are shown in Figure 12. The cutting force predictions in the Y direction show average deviations of approximately 15% and this can be attributed by transient vibrations due to the intermittent nature of the half immersion cutting.

The frequency content of the forces shows that, for low feed rates, there is more energy at the spindle frequency (1,000 Hz), compared to the forces obtained at higher feed rates because the effects of run-out and tool imperfections are more significant when the feed rate is lower. Also, there is a strong energy component (especially for forces in the Y direction) near the first mode of the system (4,000 Hz), which indicates that the second harmonic of the tooth passing frequency can excite the tool significantly and cause forced vibration. This is even more evident for half immersion conditions, since the second harmonics are stronger in this situation and cause more excitation at this frequency. Also, inspection of the frequency component of the AE sensor (Figure 13) shows that there is a large frequency component near the first mode of the system, which confirms that most of the vibration happens at the first natural frequency of the combined tool/machining centre.

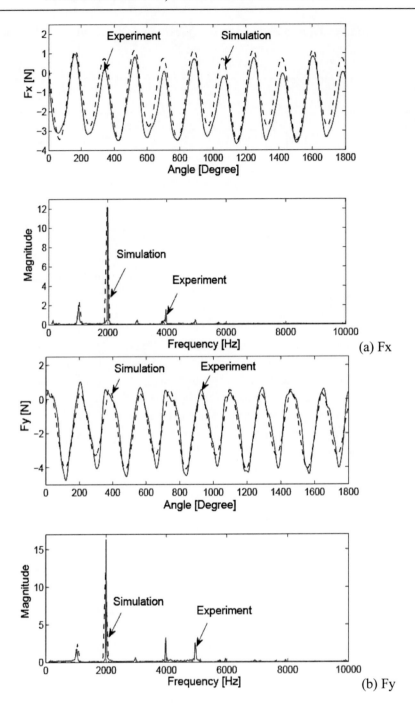

Figure 9. Comparison of forces between experiment and simulation at full immersion and feed rate of 9 µm/flute.

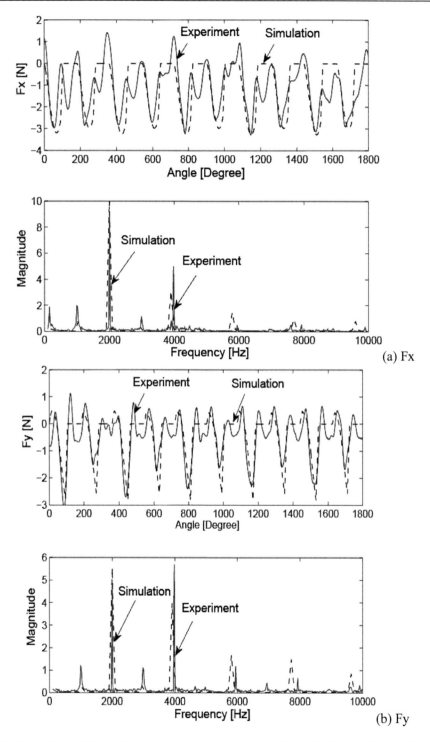

Figure 10. Comparison of forces between experiment and simulation at half immersion and feed rate of 9 µm/flute.

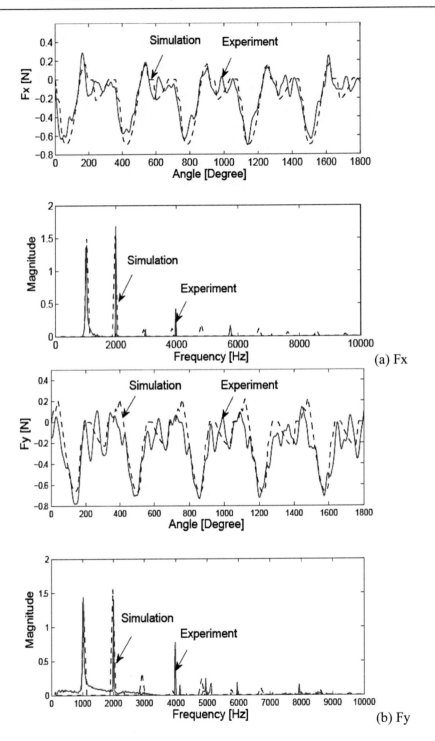

Figure 11. Comparison of forces between experiment and simulation at full immersion and feed rate of 0.5 μm/flute.

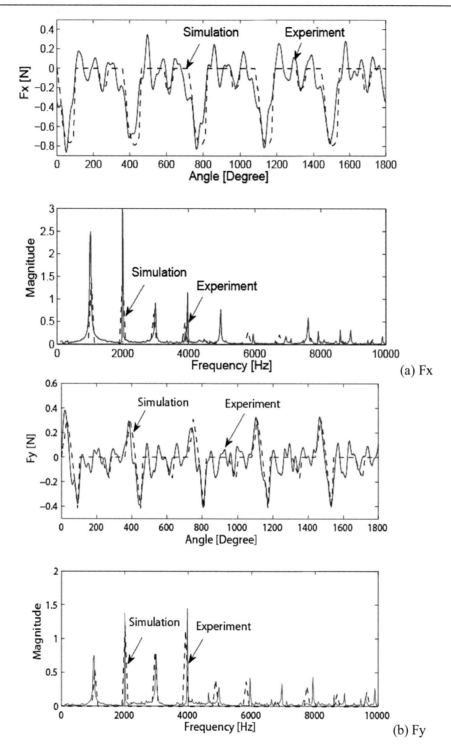

Figure 12. Comparison of forces between experiment and simulation at half immersion and feed rate of 0.5 µm/flute.

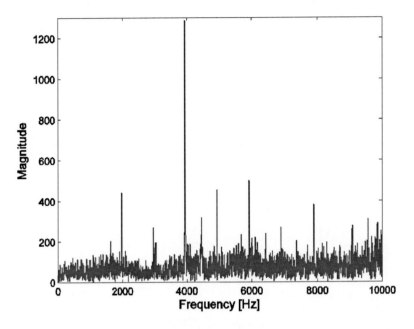

Figure 13. FFT of the AE signal for full immersion condition and feed rate of 0.5 µm/flute.

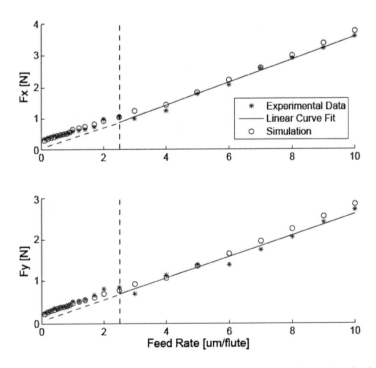

Figure 14. Comparison of the RMS of data between the experiments and simulation for full immersion condition.

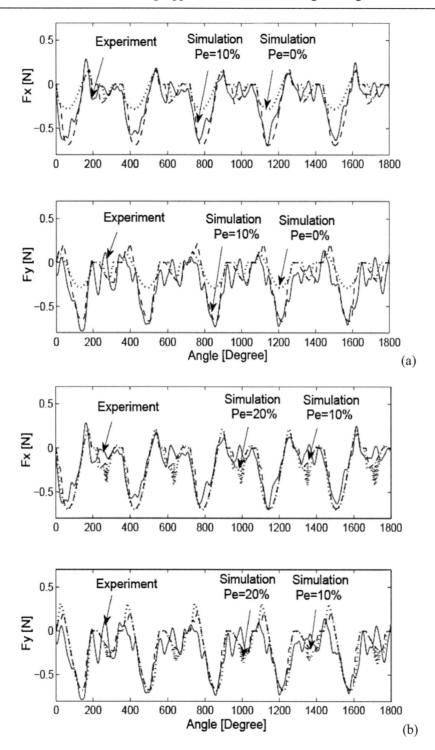

Figure 15. Comparison of forces between experiments and simulation at full immersion and a federate of 0.5 µm/flute for different run-outs: (a) $r_o = 0$ and 0.2 µm and (b) $r_o = 0.2$ and 1 µm.

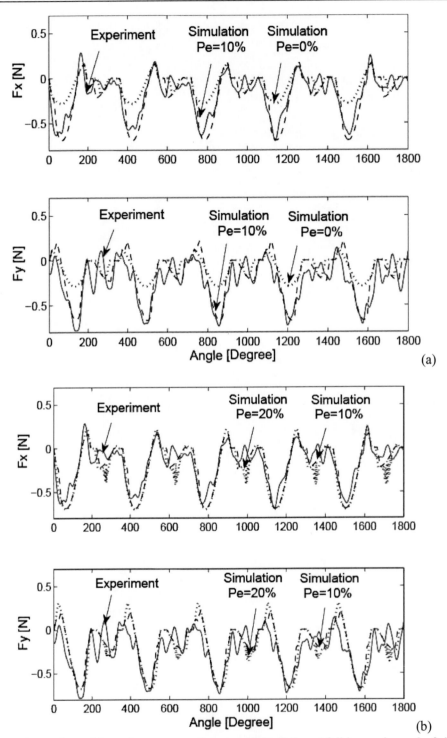

Figure 16. Comparison of forces between experiments and simulation at full immersion and a federate of 0.5 μm/flute for different elastic recoveries: (a) p_e = 0% and 10% and (b) p_e = 10% and20%.

Figure 14 shows the experimental and theoretical RMS values of the forces for both the X and Y directions with a linear curve fit of the experimental data for the shearing dominant region. The theoretical values were obtained using the developed model with the identified parameters. It can be observed that the proposed model can appropriately predict the linear behaviour in the shearing dominant regime, as well as the nonlinear behaviour, and increased forces in the ploughing dominant regime. The small deviation in the data is mainly due to the instabilities that occur during machining operations.

4. DISCUSSIONS

There are several assumptions and limitations associated with the proposed micro milling force model. The model in this paper assumes that the ploughing force is proportional to the ploughed volume of the material, which is a commonly accepted assumption by many researchers [8, 28]. Also, it is assumed in this paper that the edge force component is the same, regardless of the cutting regimes, i.e. shearing and ploughing dominant regimes. Thus, the same edge cutting coefficients are used in the mechanistic models for both the shearing and ploughing dominant regimes. An increase in the friction force due to the nonlinear interaction between ploughing and rubbing is not considered in the modeling. In this study, we performed the experimental tests using uncoated tools, and the frictional forces may be different for coated tools than for uncoated tools. Also, the workpiece is assumed to be uniform. Furthermore, tool deflection results in tilted tool conditions that may affect different parameters, such as rake angle and tool engagement. These effects, along with thermal effects, have not been considered in this study.

Utilizing the model developed in this study, the effect of different parameters, such as elastic recovery and tool run-out, could be further investigated. Figure 15 shows the actual and simulated forces for three different run-outs in full immersion and a 0.5 μm feed rate. As can be observed in Figure 15 (a), when there is no tool run-out (r_0=0), the maximum of forces is underestimated but not significantly, and the agreement between the forces becomes worse. For a run-out of 1 μm (Figure 15 (b)), there is a flat part in the force simulation, indicating that only one flute is engaged. The run-out significantly affects the forces when the feed rate is small. However, after a certain feed rate, only one flute is engaged, and the effect of increasing run-out on the cutting forces is not significant.

Figure 16 shows the effect of different elastic recovery for full immersion cutting at the feed rate of 0.5 μm. It can be observed that no elastic recovery (0% in Figure 16 (a)) exhibit smaller forces with higher deviations from the experimental results; while, for bigger elastic recovery (20% in Figure 16 (b)), slightly higher forces are predicted. The effects of run-out and elastic recovery in the shearing dominant regions are minimal and can be neglected. The experimental and theoretical forces were also compared for different depths of cut, which showed good agreement and verified the validity of the model for different cutting conditions.

5. CONCLUSION

The accurate prediction of micro milling forces is important in the determination of the optimal machining parameters, in order to prevent excessive tool wear and poor surface finish while maintaining high productivity. Unlike macro machining operations, ploughing occurs in micro machining operations when the chip thickness is less than the critical chip thickness. There have been attempts by other researchers to include the effects of ploughing, elastic recovery and the minimum chip thickness, based on slip-line plasticity or finite element modeling. However, these models are very complex, and the estimation of the many parameters in the models is difficult. A mechanistic force model has been developed for the ploughing and shearing dominant regimes for micro end milling operations, considering run-out, dynamics and the effects of the elastic recovery of material commonly encountered during micro machining. The mechanistic force model has been verified with experimental cutting force measurements of Aluminum 6061.

REFERENCES

[1]   Ehrfeld, W. and Ehrfeld, U., 2001, "Progress and profit through micro technologies. Commercial applications of MEMS/MOEMS", *Proceedings of the SPIE, 4561*, pp. 9-18.

[2]   Menz, W., Mohr, J., and Paul, O., 2001, *"Microsystem Technology"*, WILEY-VCH.

[3]   Dornfeld, D., Min, S., and Takeuchi, T., 2006, "Recent advances in mechanical micromachining", *Annals of the CIRP,* 55 (2), pp. 745-768.

[4]   Bang, Y., Lee, K., and Oh, S., 2005, "5-axis micro milling machine for machining micro parts", *International Journal of Advanced Manufacturing Technology, 25* (9-10), pp. 888-894.

[5]   Chae, J., Park, S.S., and Freiheit, T., 2006, "Investigation of Micro-Cutting Operations", *International Journal of Machine Tools and Manufacture,* 46 (3-4), pp. 313-332.

[6]   Bissacco, G., Hansen, H.N., and Slunsky, J., 2008, "Modelling the cutting edge radius size effect for force prediction in micro milling", *Annals of the CIRP,* 57 (1), pp. 113-116.

[7]   Weule, H., Huntrup, V., and Tritschle, H., 2001, "Micro-Cutting of Steel to Meet New Requirements in Miniaturization", *Annals of the CIRP,* 50 (1), pp. 61-64.

[8]   Lai, X., Li, H., Li, C., Lin, Z., and Ni, J., 2008, "Modelling and analysis of micro scale milling considering size effect, micro cutter edge radius and minimum chip thickness", *International Journal of Machine Tools and Manufacture,* 48, pp. 1-14.

[9]   Vogler, M.P., Kapoor, S.G., and DeVor, R.E., 2004, "On the Modeling and Analysis of Machining Performance in Micro end Milling, Part II: Cutting Force Prediction", *ASME Journal of Manufacturing Science and Engineering, 126* (4), pp. 695-705.

[10]   Vogler, M.P., DeVor, R.E., and Kapoor, S.G., 2004, "On the Modeling and Analysis of Machining Performance in Micro end Milling, Part I: Surface Generation", *ASME Journal of Manufacturing Science and Engineering,* 126 (4), pp. 685-694.

[11]   Armarego, E.J.A. and Brown, R.H., 1962, "On Size Effect in Metal Cutting", *International Journal of Production Research,* 1(3), pp. 75-99.

[12]   Lucca, D.A., Rhorer, R.L., and Komanduri, R., 1991, "Energy Dissipation in the Ultraprecision Machining of Copper", *Annals of the CIRP,* 40 (1), pp. 69-72.

[13] Komanduri, R., 1971, "Some Aspects of Machining with Negative Rake Tools Simulating Grinding", *International Journal of Machine Tool Design, 11* (3), pp. 223-233.

[14] Waldorf, D.J., DeVor, R.E., and Kapoor, S.G., 1998, "Slip-Line Field for Ploughing During Orthogonal Cutting", *ASME Journal of Manufacturing Science and Engineering,* 120 (4), pp. 693-698.

[15] Jun, M.B.G., Liu, X., DeVor, R.E., and Kapoor, S.G., 2006, "Investigation of the Dynamics of Micro end Milling, Part 1: Model Development", *ASME Journal of Manufacturing Science and Engineering,* 128 (4), pp. 893-900.

[16] Fang, N., 2003, "Slip-Line Modeling of Machining with a Rounded-Edge Tool - Part I: New Model and Theory", *Journal of the Mechanics and Physics of Solids, 51* (4), pp. 715-742.

[17] Liu, K. and Melkote, S.N., 2006, "Material Strengthening Mechanisms and Their Contribution to Size Effect in Micro-Cutting", *ASME Journal of Manufacturing Science and Engineering,* 128 (3), pp. 730-738.

[18] Kim, K.W., Lee, W.Y., and Sin, H.C., 1999, "Finite Element Analysis for the Characteristics of Temperature and Stress in Micro-Machining Considering the Size Effect", *International Journal of Machine Tools and Manufacture,* 39 (9), pp. 1507-1524.

[19] Ozel, T. and Zeren, E. 2005, "Finite Element Modeling of Stresses Induced by High Speed Machining with Round Edge Cutting Tools", 2005 ASME International Mechanical Engineering Congress and Exposition, *IMECE* 2005, Nov 5-11 2005. Orlando, FL, United States.

[20] Rech, J., Yen, Y.-C., Schaff, M.J., Hamdi, H., Altan, T., and Bouzakis, K.D., 2005, "Influence of Cutting Edge Radius on the Wear Resistance of Pm-Hss Milling Inserts", *Wear,* 259 (7-12), pp. 1168-1176.

[21] Zaman, M.T., Kumar, A.S., Rahman, M., and Sreeram, S., 2006, "A Three-Dimensional Analytical Cutting Force Model for Micro End Milling Operation", *International Journal of Machine Tools and Manufacture,* 46 (3-4), pp. 353-366.

[22] Bao, W.Y. and Tansel, I.N., 2000, "Modeling Micro end-Milling Operations. Part I: Analytical Cutting Force Model", International *Journal of Machine Tools and Manufacture,* 40 (15), pp. 2155-2173.

[23] Kang, I.S., Kim, J.S., Kim, J.H., Kang, M.C., and Seo, Y.W., 2007, "A mechanistic model of cutting force in the micro end milling process", *Journal of Materials Processing Technology,* 187-188, pp. 250-255.

[24] Lee, H.U., Cho, D.W., and Ehmann, K.F., 2008, "A mechanistic model of cutting forces in micro-end-milling with cutting-condition-independent cutting force coefficients", *ASME Journal of Manufacturing Science and Engineering,* 130 (3), pp. 0311021-0311029.

[25] Malekian, M., Park, S. S., Jun, M. B. G., 2009, "Modeling of dynamic micro-milling cutting forces", *International Journal of Machine Tools and Manufacture,* 29, pp. 586-598.

[26] Basuray, P. K., Misra, B. K., Lal, G. K., 1977, "Transition from Ploughing to Cutting during Machining with Blunt Tools", *Wear,* 43 (3), pp. 341-349.

[27] Malekian, M. and Park, S.S., 2007, "Investigation of Micro Milling Forces for Aluminum," *Transactions of SME - NAMRI,* 35 (1), pp. 417-424.

[28] Wu, D.W., 1989, "A New Approach of Formulating the Transfer Function for Dynamic Cutting Processes", *ASME Journal of Engineering for Industry, 111*, pp. 37-47.

[29] Endres, W.J., DeVor, R.E., and Kapoor, S.G., 1995, "Dual-Mechanism Approach to the Prediction of Machining Forces, Part 1: Model Development", *ASME Journal of Engineering for Industry,* 117 (4), pp. 526-533.

[30] Shawky, A.M. and Elbestawi, M.A., 1997, "Enhanced Dynamic Model in Turning Including the Effect of Ploughing Forces", *ASME Journal of Manufacturing Science and Engineering, 119* (1), pp. 10-20.

[31] Elbestawi, M.A., Ismail, F., Du, R., and Ullagaddi, B.C., 1994, "Modelling Machining Dynamics Including Damping in the Tool-Workpiece Interface", *ASME Journal of Engineering for Industry,* 116 (4), pp. 435-439.

[32] Jun, M.B.G., DeVor, R.E., and Kapoor, S.G., 2006, "Investigation of the Dynamics of Micro end Milling, Part 2: Model Validation and Interpretation", *ASME Journal of Manufacturing Science and Engineering,* 128 (4), pp. 901-912.

[33] Altintas, Y., 2000, *"Manufacturing Automation",* Cambridge University Press.

[34] Mascardelli, B.A., Park, S.S., and Freiheit, T., 2006, "Substructure Coupling of Micro end Mills", ASME International Mechanical Engineering Congress and Exposition, *IMECE2006.* Chicago, IL, United States.

[35] Schmitz, T.L., and Duncan, G.S., 2006, "Receptance coupling for dynamics prediction of assemblies with coincident neutral axes", *Journal of Sound and Vibration,* 289, pp. 1045-65.

[36] Altintas, Y., Park, S.S., 2004, "Dynamic Compensation of Spindle Integrated Force Sensors", *Annals of CIRP,* 53 (1), pp. 305-309.

[37] Adby, P.R and Dempster, M.A.H., 1974, *"Introduction to Optimization Methods",* London, Chapman and Hall.

[38] Malekian, M., Park, S.S, and Um, K., 2008, "Investigation of Micro Plowing Forces through Conical Scratch Tests", *Transactions of SME - NAMRI,* 36 (1), pp. 293-300.

In: Micro and Nanomanufacturing Research
Editor: J. Paulo Davim

ISBN 978-1-61942-003-8
© 2012 Nova Science Publishers, Inc.

Chapter 3

A STUDY ON SURFACE QUALITY IN MICROMILLING

Pedro Cardoso, J. Paulo Davim [*]

Department of Mechanical Engineering, University of Aveiro
Campus Santiago, 3810-193 Aveiro, Portugal

ABSTRACT

The demand for miniaturized devices with high aspect ratios and superior surfaces has been rapidly increasing in aerospace, automotive, biomedical, optical, military and micro-electronics packaging industries. In the present chapter, the machining of micro surfaces on aluminium alloy is made, using conventional machines and commercially available miniature tools. In order to perform a comprehensive study on the quality of the machined surfaces (roughness, accuracy and burrs), machining parameters such as feed rate were varied. Also, a variety of machining strategies was performed in order to study the quality of the machined surfaces.

1. INTRODUCTION

Micromilling is a process that utilizes end mills that typically vary in diameter from 100 to 1000 μm and have edge radii that vary from 1 to 10 μm. Additionally, the micromilling process has several salient features that differentiate it from the macro-endmilling process. As the endmilling process is scaled down from conventional sizes (100 μm/tooth feed rates, 1 mm depths of cut) to micro-endmilling sizes (1 μm/tooth feed rates, 100 μm depths of cut), different phenomena dominate the micro-endmilling process compared to those typically observed in conventional milling (Vogler et al., 2004; Bissacco et al, 2005; Kang et al 2007)). Dhanorker and Özel (2008) stated that the fundamental difference between micromilling and

---

[*] Corresponding author, E-mail: pdavim@ua.pt

conventional milling arises due to scale of the operation, in spite of being kinematically the same. However, the ratio of feed per tooth to radius of the cutter is much greater in micromilling than conventional milling, which often leads to an error in predicting cutting forces. Also, the runout of the tool tip, even within microns, greatly affects the accuracy of micromilling as opposed to the conventional milling.

The chip formation in micromilling depends upon a minimum chip thickness and hence the chip is not always formed whenever tool and workpiece is engaged as opposed to conventional milling. The tool deflection in the micromilling greatly affects the chip formation and accuracy of the desired surface as compared to conventional milling. The tool edge radius (typically between 1–5 µm) and its uniformity along the cutting edge are highly important as the chip thickness becomes a comparable in size to the cutting edge radius (Aramcharoen et al. 2008). Since the chip load is small compared to the cutting edge radius, the size effect and ploughing forces become significant on both surface and force generation in micromilling. Micromilling may result in surface generation with burrs and increased roughness due to the ploughing-dominated cutting and side flow of the deformed material when the cutting edge becomes worn and blunter (Filiz Sinan et al, 2007; Liu et al, 2004; Ng Chee Keong et al, 2006).

The effect of machining strategies and cutting parameters on surface roughness, accuracy and burrs has been analysed in this work.

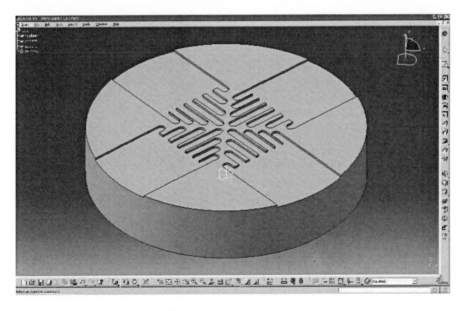

Figure 1. Example of part design in CATIA.

2. EXPERIMENTAL PROCEDURE

2.1. CAD/CAM Software

Figure 1 represents the surface that was designed using CATIA® (Computer Aided Three Dimensional Interactive Application), to perform the machining tests present in this work.

After designing the surface in CATIA®, the 3D model was then imported into Mastercam®. All important parameters were entered in Mastercam®: end mill diameter, depth of cut, feed per tooth, spindle speed and cutting speed. After these parameters were entered, the three different machining strategies were defined and simulated. All three strategies are depicted in Figure 2.

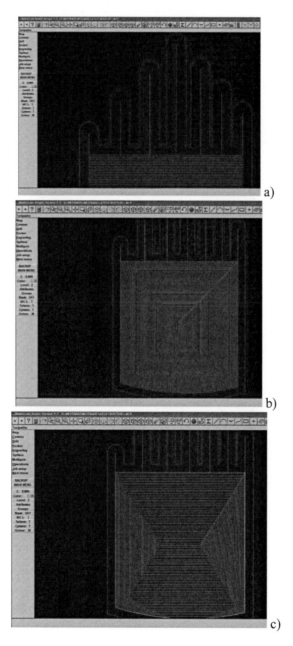

a)

b)

c)

Figure 2. a) Parallel zigzag toolpath, b) Constant overlap spiral toolpath c) Parallel spiral toolpath.

Figure 3. The chuck fastened to the CNC table holding the workpiece.

2. EXPERIMENTAL SETUP

To perform the machining, the CNC milling centre used was MIKRON model VCE 500. It is a conventional, full size, 11 kW, 3-axis CNC milling centre with maximum travel of 500 x 400 x 500 mm. Spindle speed can range between 60 and 7500 rpm and has a tool holder capable of 20 different tools. Figure 3 represents the chuck fastened to the CNC table, holding the workpiece

The tool used to machine the workpiece was a cemented carbide Sandvik® Plura mini, general purpose, 0.8 mm diameter endmill. Figure 4 presents a photograph of 0.8mm tool

2.3. Workpiece Material

Al 2011 is an Al-Cu-Bi-Pb age-hardenable alloy noted for its free-machining characteristics and good mechanical properties. Since it is an excellent all round alloy, it is used in many applications, such as: adapters, clock parts and gears, knobs, camera parts, meter shafts and gears, nozzles, pencil and pen parts, oil line filters, pipe stems and filters, radio parts, screwdriver caps, spindles, telephone parts, TV fittings, tripod fittings, machine parts, hose parts, etc.

2.4. Cutting Parameters / Machining Strategies

In this experiment, several samples were machined, varying feed rate and strategy between them. The only three constants between samples were spindle speed, that was kept constant at 6500 rpm which, with the 0.8 mm diameter endmill used, results in a constant cutting speed of 16.3 m/min, toolpath overlap, which was also kept constant at 0.05mm and, finally, depth of cut 0.2 mm

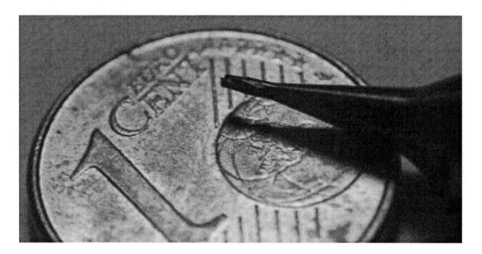

Figure 4. Photograph of 0.8mm endmill.

Table 1. Summary of machining parameters, 6500 rpm and ap=0.2mm

Strategy	Feed rate mm/tooth
1 Constant overlap spiral	0.002
	0.004
	0.006
	0.008
2 Parallel spiral	0.002
	0.004
	0.006
	0.008
3 Parallel zigzag	0.002
	0.004
	0.006
	0.008

The three strategies, first simulated in Mastercam®, were chosen based on the current most common ways to mill a pocket, so they were: parallel zigzag, constant overlap spiral and parallel spiral. In order to obtain a wide gamut of results from this experience, four feed rates were used for each strategy. Table 1 shows a summary of the strategies and parameters used to machine the samples.

2. SURFACE QUALITY CHARACTERIZATION

For the qualitative characterization of the surface quality, an optical microscope was used. In this analysis, the magnification used for the acquisition of all the images of all the surfaces was 50x.

In order to characterize the surface profile, a profilometer was used. This equipment measures a number of standard surface roughness parameters (Ra, Rz, Rt, Rmax, R3z, etc). Dependent upon the type of parameter measured, these surface roughness values are calculated from the unfiltered, measured profile, the filtered roughness profile or the filtered waviness profile.

The most relevant surface roughness parameters considered were *Rt* and *RzI*. *Rt* is the vertical distance from the deepest valley to the highest peak and *RzI* is a parameter that averages the height of the five highest peaks plus the depth of the five deepest valleys over the evaluation length.

Two measurements were made for each sample, in order to obtain an average value of all the surface quality parameters.

3. RESULTS AND DISCUSSION

In order to qualitatively analyze surface quality in all the machined samples, many photographs were taken to observe the burr formation between different feed rates and strategies used. Figure 5 shows an overview of some samples machined.

Figure 5. Overview of the machined samples compared to a 0.5 mm pencil lead.

Figure 6 thru 8 show the comparison between the four different feed rates in all the three strategies described in the previous section. The photos depict the two thinnest details in all samples.

From Figure 6, it can be said that the amount of burrs produced is not very high, although not insignificant; (a) and (b) show a small exit burr on the widest fin, (c) shows quite a large exit burr, but (d), which represents the highest feed rate, shows a very large, and very pronounced burr on the widest fin. In addition, and on the contrary to the other feed rates, the thinnest fin in (d) also shows a small deflection close to the end.

The burrs produced with the second strategy, shown next in Figure 7, are much more pronounced. Again, feed rate of 8μm/tooth is the one that shows more burr formation. Also to note that, in this strategy, the deflection of the thinnest fin is significantly larger than with the previous strategy.

Finally, Figure 8 shows the same details of the previous figures, but for the last machining strategy, parallel zigzag. In this case, burrs can be considered similar to the previous strategy, but the observed deflection in the thinnest profile is severely increased in comparison with the other two strategies.

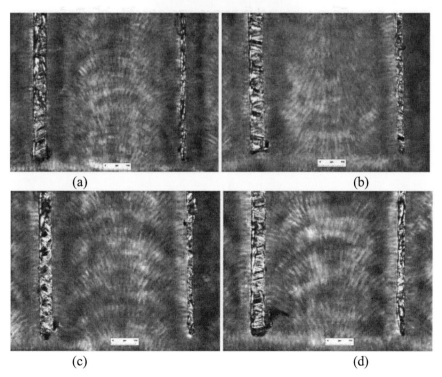

(a) (b)

(c) (d)

Figure 6. Strategy 1, constant overlap spiral, at different feed rates: (a) 2 μm/tooth, (b) 4μm/tooth, (c) 6 μm/tooth and (d) 8 μm/tooth.

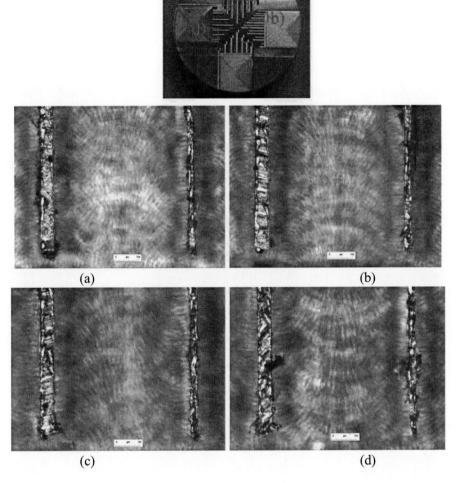

Figure 7. Strategy 2, parallel spiral, at different feed rates : (a) 2 μm/tooth, (b) 4μm/tooth, (c) 6 μm/tooth and (d) 8 μm/tooth.

As previously stated, surface roughness profile were measured in a profilometer. Surface roughness profile comparison between strategies for an example of feed rate is presented in Figure 9.

From the values obtained from the measurement of the surface roughness parameters, several charts were plotted in order to obtain the relationships between feed rates and Rt and RzI. Figure 10 shows the RzI evolution with feed rate for each strategy. Strategy 1 and 3 are very close together, but, with this parameter, strategy 3 actually performs worse than strategy 2 when f = 4μm/tooth. Strategy 1 maintains an almost constant value of RzI = 0.7μm, except for f= 8μm/tooth, where it rises up to RzI = 0.8μm. It is, however, the strategy that averages the best results for values of RzI.

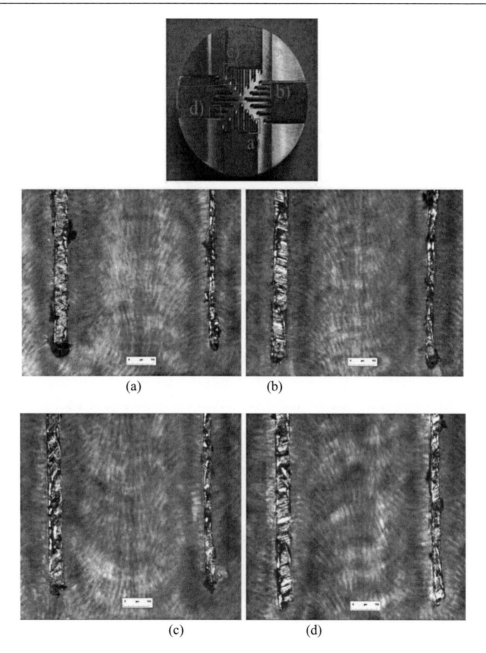

Figure 8. Strategy 3 parallel zigzag, at different feed rates: (a) 2 µm/tooth, (b) 4µm/tooth, (c) 6 µm/tooth and (d) 8 µm/tooth.

From this chart, one can see that all strategies deliver a very wide gamut of Rt values, ranging from Rt = 0.80µm in strategy 1 and 3 to Rt = 1.30µm in strategy 2. Once again, strategy 1 is the best performer, delivering the best results for each one of the feed rates. Only strategy 3 gets close, when f = 2µm/tooth, but even at that point, strategy 1 delivers a lower Rt than strategy 3.

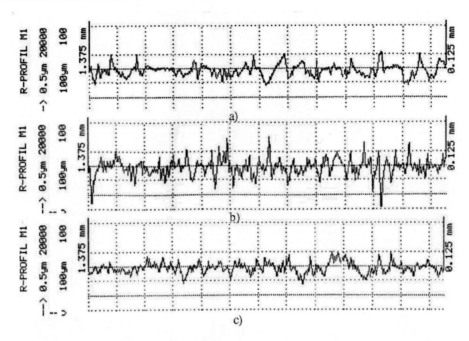

Figure 9. Surface profile comparison between strategies for the same feed rate of 2 µm /tooth: a) constant overlap spiral, b) parallel spiral and c) parallel zigzag.

For the values of Rt, the vertical distance from the deepest valley to the highest peak, Figure 11 depicts its variation with feed rate for each strategy, once again.

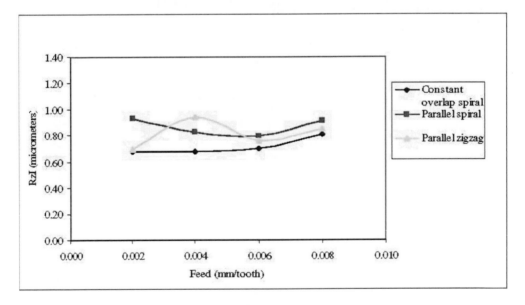

Figure 10. RzI evolution with feed rate for each strategy.

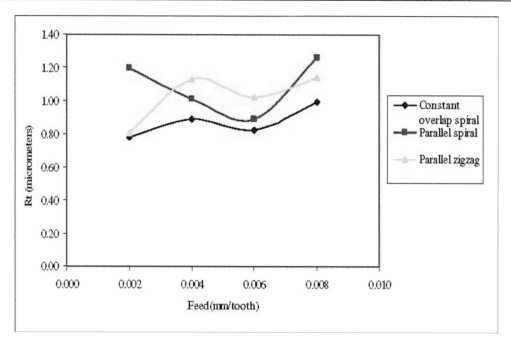

Figure 11. Rt evolution with feed rate for each strategy.

4. CONCLUSIONS

This chapter had as a goal the experimental validation of surface micro machining with conventional CNC machine tools and micro tools. With this work it was assessed that it is possible to micro mill surfaces with a conventional CNC machine tool, using micro tools and special fixture devices for the workpiece.

During the experiment, it was also observed that the strategy chosen to machine the samples together with the chosen feed rate values are fundamental to achieve good surface finish results. In this study, the strategy with which it was achieved the best results was strategy "constant overlap spiral". It was also observed that the highest feed rates delivered the best quality surfaces, i.e., 6 and 8 µm/tooth. Regarding burr formation, the feed rate that presented the surface with the least amount of burrs was 6µm/tooh. The optical analysis of the machined samples revealed that it is possible to achieve machined micro surfaces almost without burrs.

ACKNOWLEDGMENTS

The authors would like to thanks for MSc A. Festas for the technical assistance during the experimental work.

REFERENCES

Aramcharoen A., Mativenga P.T., Yang S., Cooke K.E., Teer D.G. (2008) Evaluation and selection of hard coatings for micro milling of hardened tool steel, *International Journal of Machine Tools & Manufacture* 48, 1578– 1584.

Bissacco G., Hansen H.N., Chiffre L. De (2005) Micromilling of hardened tool steel for mould making applications, *Journal of Materials Processing Technology* 167, 201–207.

Dhanorker A., Özel T. (2008) Meso/micro scale milling for micro-manufacturing, *Int. J. Mechatronics and Manufacturing Systems,* Vol. 1, No. 1, 23-42.

Filiz Sinan, Xie Luke, Weiss Lee E., Ozdoganlar O.B. (2007) Micromilling of microbarbs for medical implants, *International Journal of Machine Tools & Manufacture* 48, 459–472.

Kang I.S., Kim J.S., Kim J.H., Kang M.C., Seo Y.W. (2007) A mechanistic model of cutting force in the micro end milling process, *Journal of Materials Processing Technology 187–188*, 250–255.

Liu X., DeVor R.E., Kapoor S.G., Egmann K.F. (2004) The Mechanics of Machining at the Microscale: Assessment of the Current State of the Science, *Journal of Manufacturing Science and Engineering,* November, Vol. 126, 666-678.

Ng Chee Keong, Melkote Shreyes N., Rahman M., Kumar A. Senthil (2006) *Experimental study of micro-and nano-scale cutting of aluminum* 7075-T6, International Journal of Machine Tools & Manufacture 46, 929–936.

Vogler Michael P., DeVor Richard E., Kapoor Shiv G. (2004) On the Modelling and Analysis of Machining Performance in Micro-Endmilling, Part I: Surface Generation, *Journal of Manufacturing Science and Engineering November*, Vol. 126, 685-694.

In: Micro and Nanomanufacturing Research
Editor: J. Paulo Davim

ISBN 978-1-61942-003-8
© 2012 Nova Science Publishers, Inc.

Chapter 4

NUMERICAL SIMULATION AND EXPERIMENTAL VALIDATION WHEN PRECISION RADIAL TURNING AISI 1045 STEEL

P. Faria[1], J. Paulo Davim[2,], C. Maranhão[2], Leonardo R. Silva[3], A. Abrão[3], J. Campos Rubio[1]*

[1]Department of Mechanical Engineering, University of Minas Gerais, Campus Pampulha, 31.270-901, Belo Horizonte, Minas Gerais, Brazil
[2]Department of Mechanical Engineering, University of Aveiro, Campus Santiago, 3810-193, Aveiro, Portugal
[3]Department of Mechanics, Federal Center for Technological Education of Minas Gerais, Av. Amazonas, 5253, Nova Suíça, 30.480-000, Belo Horizonte, Minas Gerais, Brazil

ABSTRACT

Finite element method (FEM) models when applied to machining operations aid the understanding of the principal phenomena involved in machining. The present work deals with FEM simulations and compares the results with data obtained through either experimental or analytical methods. The subject matter is precision radial turning of AISI 1045 medium carbon steel with uncoated carbide tools under a fixed cutting condition. The following aspects were investigated: cutting and thrust forces, cutting temperature and plastic strain. In general, the results suggest that the value experimental (analytical) and numerical were next.

---

* Corresponding author, E-mail: pdavim@ua.pt

1. INTRODUCTION

FEM simulations applied to metal cutting operations are capable of providing comprehensive information with regard to the chip formation mechanism (and, as a consequence, on the shear angle and chip thickness), temperature distribution at the chip-tool interface, cutting forces, cutting-edge deformation in the cutting region and stresses on the cutting edge, which lead to the evolution of tool wear. Using bidimensional machining models, the cutting tool is parameterized by its rake and clearance angles and cutting edge radius, in addition to general chip breaker geometries and workpiece dimensions. Numerical and experimental studies were conducted by Kim et al [1] in order to establish the influence of the cutting tool edge when turning a low carbon steel. Orthogonal cutting experiments confirmed that the size effect is drastically affected by the tool edge radius and a satisfactory agreement between numerical and experimental results was obtained. According with Mamalis et al [2], the equivalent orthogonal cutting model predicts satisfactorily the values of the cutting force, but significantly underestimates the thrust force, thus indicating that the use of three dimensional finite element cutting models capable of taking into account the varying chip cross section and the tool edge radius are necessary in order to achieve more accurate results. Qian and Mohammad [3] studied the influence of the work material hardness, cutting parameters and tool geometry when finish hard turning using numerical simulations and experimental work. These researchers concluded that the forces have a trend to increase with higher feed rate, tool nose radius, negative rake angles, and workpiece hardness. These results are consistent with experimental and numerical investigations reported by other researchers. Grzesik et al [4] investigated the variation of the temperature gradient using a finite element method and compared the findings with data obtained from experimental turning of AISI 1045 with uncoated and coated cutting tools and a good agreement between experimental and numerical results was achieved. An investigation into the tool-chip contact interface using uncoated tungsten-based cemented carbide tools in dry high speed turning of AISI 1045 steel carried out by Iqbal et al [5] showed that simulations with finite element method depend mainly on the value of the friction coefficient (employed as an input value within the software) to obtain precise values. The simulation of the chip formation, temperature distribution as well as predictions of the stress distributions in the chip, tool and on the machined surface were successfully achieved for AISI 1045 steel. Umbrello et al [6] simulated and measured the coefficient of global heat transfer for AISI 1045 steel and proposed a rule to adjust the simulated and experimental data.

Özel and Zeren [7] presented a numerical modelling approach based on explicit dynamic Arbitrary Lagrangian Eulerian method with adaptive meshing capability and developed simulation models for meso-scale finish machining of AISI 1045, AISI 4340 steels and Ti6Al4V titanium alloy using finite edge radius carbide cutting tool without employing a remeshing scheme and without using a chip separation criterion. The numerical modelings show the development of temperature distributions during the cutting process. Very high and localized temperatures are predicted at tool-chip interface due to a detailed friction model. Predictions of the von Mises stress distributions in the chip, in the tool and on the machined surface are effectively carried out. Process induced stress profiles depict that there exist both compressive and tensile stress regions beneath the surface. The authors say predictions combined with the temperature field predictions are highly essential to further predict surface integrity and thermo-mechanical deformation related property alteration on the microstructure of the machined surfaces.

Outeiro [8] studied the influence of RTS (Relative Tool Sharpness) on the cutting process analytically and experimentally and conclude that to minimize the influence of the tool cutting edge radius in the cutting process RTS should be kept higher than that of the critical RTScritical.

In the following analysis, numerical simulations using *Advantedge*^{TM} (a Lagrangian finite element-based machining model) were performed to predict cutting and thrust forces, temperature distribution and plastic strain in the chip and work material. The software uses an explicit dynamic, thermo-mechanically coupled finite element method and employs adaptive re-meshing to resolve highly distorted meshes. The FEM simulation results were compared with experimental data (in the case of the cutting and thrust forces) and with findings obtained analytically (maximum cutting temperature and plastic strain).

2. EXPERIMENTAL PROCEDURE

Radial turning tests using bars of AISI 1045 steel with 20 mm in diameter and 80 mm long as work material were carried out with uncoated cemented carbide tools (Sandvik N151.2-540-40-3B H13A). Figures 1 and 2 show, respectively, a schematic diagram of the operation and photographs of the workpiece and tool used in the experimental work. The chemical composition and thermal and mechanical properties of AISI 1045 steel are given in Table 1. Dry turning tests were performed on a Kingsbury MHP 50 CNC lathe with 18 kW spindle power and a maximum spindle speed of 4500 rpm. A *Kistler*$^{®}$ piezoelectric dynamometer model 9121 with a load amplifier connected to a computer was used for the acquisition of the cutting force (F_c) and thrust force (F_t). The following cutting condition was used: cutting speed of 70 m/min, feed rate of 80 μm/rev and width of cut of 2.7 mm.

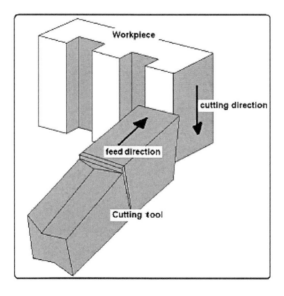

Figure 1. Schematic diagram of the radial turning operation.

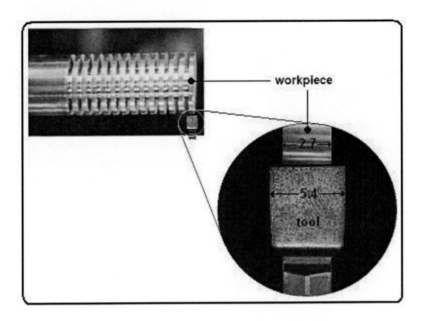

Figure 2. Workpiece and cutting tool used in radial turning operation.

Table 1. Chemical composition and thermal and mechanical properties of AISI 1045 steel

Chemical Composition (%)	
C	0.45
Mn	0.65
Si	0.25
Thermal Properties	
Thermal conductivity (W/mK)	49.8
Specific heat capacity (J/kg°C)	486
Mechanical Properties	
Density (kg/mm³)	7.85
Hardness (HB)	205
Elongation (%)	≥18
Modulus of elasticity (GPa)	205
Yield strength (MPa)	≥360
Tensile strength (MPa)	600 - 720

In order to calculate the cutting temperature and the plastic strain, Boothroyd and Knight [9] and Merchant [10] models were used, respectively.

These results obtained experimentally (cutting and thrust forces) and analytically (cutting temperature and plastic strain) were compared with those obtained from the FEM simulation work and the percentage difference was calculated through Equation (1):

$$\Delta(\%) = \frac{\left| V_{exp} - V_{fem} \right|}{V_{exp}} \times 100 \tag{1}$$

Where V_{exp} is the value obtained either experimentally or analytically and V_{fem} is the value from the FEM machining simulation.

Table 2. Simulation parameters used on the finite element model

Workpiece Parameters	
Workpiece material	AISI 1045
Workpiece length [mm]	2.5
Workpiece height [mm]	2
Tool Parameters	
Tool material	Uncoated carbide tool
Clearance angle [°]	7
Rake angle [°]	0
Cutting edge radius [mm]	0.02
Rake face length [mm]	1
Relief face length [mm]	1
Cutting Parameters	
Cutting speed [m/min]	70
Feed rate [μm/ rev]	80
Width of cut [mm]	2.7
Lenght of cut [mm]	2.5
Room temperature [°C]	20
Friction coefficient (*)	0.428
(**)	0.2
Simulation	
Maximum number of nodes	12000
Maximum element size [mm]	0.1
Minimum element size [mm]	0.02

* value obtained experimentally.
** value obtained from interactions.

3. FINITE ELEMENTS ANALYSIS

Simulations were performed with *Third Wave Systems AdvantEdge*[TM] machining simulation software, which integrates advanced finite element model appropriate for machining operations. The orthogonal cutting system is described in Figure 3 and a sample of the software output is given in Figure 4. The finite element model was used to simulate orthogonal cutting (radial turning) of AISI 1045 steel with using uncoated carbide tools. The work material properties were determined using the FEM program database.

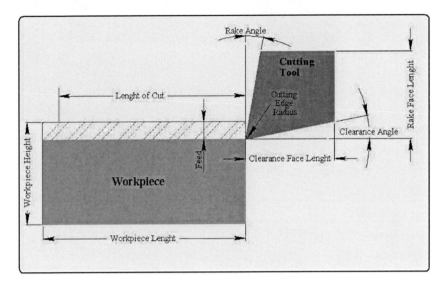

Figure 3. Schematic of finite element model taken from the software.

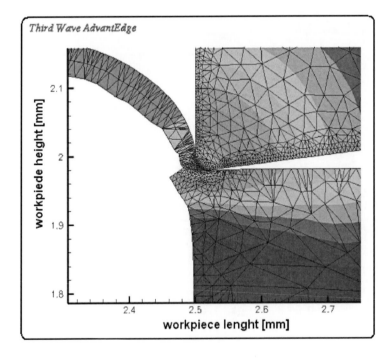

Figure 4. Sample of the finite element model mesh.

The principal parameters that affect the simulation results are the friction coefficient, work and tool material properties and cutting geometry [11, 12]. The input parameters entered into the code are given in Table 3. The friction coefficient (μ) used in the FEM analysis was obtained applying the cutting and thrust forces values obtained experimentally to Equation (2), thus resulting in μ=0.428. On the other hand, the friction coefficient is the starting point for the FEM model, thus several iterations were conducted in order to find a friction coefficient able to simulate cutting and thrust forces as close as possible to the experimental values. As a result, a friction coefficient of μ=0.2 was also used in the simulation work.

$$\mu = \frac{F_t + F_c tg\gamma}{F_c - F_t tg\gamma}$$ (2)

Where F_c is the cutting force, F_t is the thrust force and γ is the rake angle.

Table 3. Experimental/analytical and FEM simulated values for distinct friction coefficients

	Experimental/ Analytical	FEM μ=0.428		FEM μ=0.2	
	Value	Value	Δ (%)	Value	Δ (%)
Cutting force (N)	495.52	684.54	38.1	578.79	16.8
Thrust force (N)	212.17	361.71	70.5	223.62	5.4
Temperature (°C)	404.4	455.8	12.7	419.16	3.6
Plastic strain	4.37	4.54	4.0	4.25	2.7

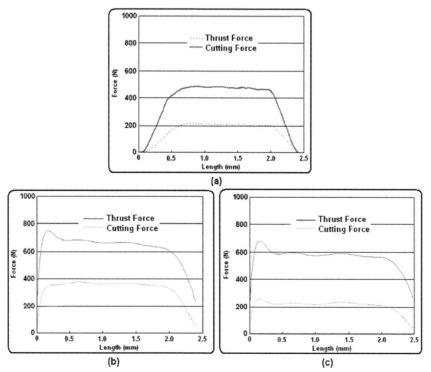

Figure 5. Cutting and thrust forces values: (a) experimental results, (b) FEM results for a friction coefficient of 0.428 and (c) FEM results for a friction coefficient of 0.2.

4. Results and Discussion

Table 4 presents an overview of the principal results concerning the experimental cutting and thrust forces and the analytical cutting temperature and plastic strain. Additionally, the results of the FEM simulations considering friction coefficients of 0.428 and 0.2 are presented together with the percentage difference between experimental/analytical and numerical results. These results are depicted in the next sections, however, it can be noticed that a friction coefficient of µ=0.2 is responsible for the smallest difference between the experimental/analytical and numerical data. This result was not expected and may attributed to the fact that, during actual machining, seizure and sliding are likely to take place, therefore, the average friction coefficient calculated from Equation (2) may not be appropriate to be employed in the numerical work.

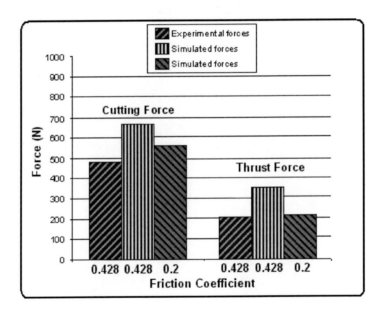

Figure 6. Average cutting and thrust forces obtained analytically and by FEM simulations using distinct friction coefficients.

4.1. Cutting and Thrust Forces

Figure 5 shows the experimental (Figure 5a) and numerical simulation (Figures 5b and 5c) results concerning the cutting and thrust forces as a function of the length of cut. The FEM simulation results are presented for the two friction coefficients tested: µ=0,428 (Figure 5b) and µ=0,2 (Figure 5c). It can be noticed that while the experimental forces remain unaltered throughout the whole cutting length, the cutting forces obtained via the FEM model tend to decrease slightly during the simulation. The average cutting and thrust force values were, respectively, 495.52 N and 212.17 N, see Figure 6. The difference between experimental and numerical results for a for a friction coefficient µ=0.428 was Δ=38.1% (cutting force) and Δ=70.5% (thrust force), whereas for µ=0.2 the difference was 16.8% and 5.4%, respectively. The reason for such differences between experimental and simulated values may reside in the fact that the temperature estimated by the software is lower than the actual temperature in the shear plane. Consequently, the shear yield strength during the experimental work will be lower than its numerical counterpart, thus requiring lower cutting and thrust forces.

Furthermore, as previously mentioned, conditions of seizure and sliding are likely to take place during machining trials using steel as work material due to the fact that near the cutting edge the normal force is high enough to make the real contact area close to become a considerable proportion of the apparent area. Under these circumstances, the real area of contact is independent of the normal force and the frictional force is that required to shear the work material. As a conclusion, the friction coefficient calculated as indicated in Equation (2) cannot represent, alone, the phenomena involved in the chip-tool interface.

4.2. Cutting Temperature

Figure 7 shows the simulation maps with the cutting temperature at the end of the cutting length of cut. The maximum cutting temperature calculated analytically using [9] and the FEM simulation results are compared in Figure 8. It can be noted by observing the isotherms that higher temperatures are obtained using the higher friction coefficient and, as indicated in Table 4, the difference between the analytical and numerical temperatures varies with the friction coefficient ($\Delta=12.7\%$ for $\mu=0.428$ and $\Delta=3.6\%$ for $\mu=0.2$). Unfortunately, without the experimental evaluation of the cutting temperature one cannot conclude how close the analytical and numerical are to the actual cutting temperature, mainly due to the fact that accurate values for the proportion of heat generated in the shear zone and conducted into the workpiece and for the contact length between the chip and the rake face cannot be easily obtained.

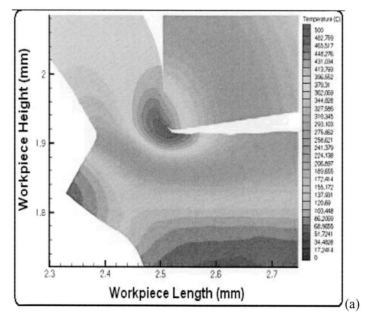

(a)

Figure 7. (Continued).

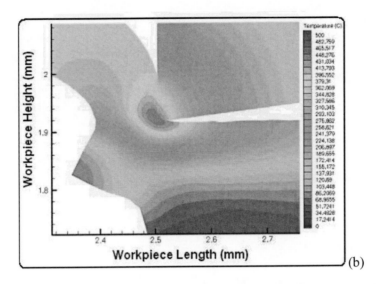

Figure 7. Cutting temperature simulation at the end of the cutting length: (a) friction coefficients of 0.428 and (b) friction coefficient of 0.2.

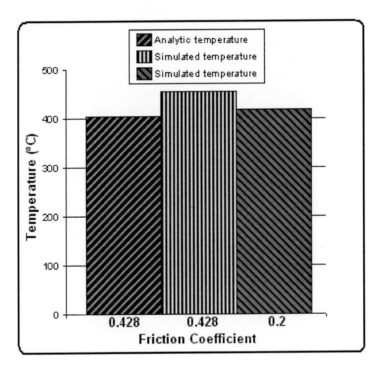

Figure 8. Maximum cutting temperature obtained analytically and by FEM simulations using distinct friction coefficients.

4.3. Plastic Strain

Figure 9 shows the simulation maps with the evolution of the plastic strain in the chip and machined surface for the two friction coefficients employed in the simulation work. Not surprisingly, μ=0.428 was responsible for inducing more severe strain in the chip and workpiece due to the increased restriction to chip flow. Figure 10 compares the analytical plastic strain and the results from the FEM simulation. In this case the results were near and the difference was 4.7% and 2.7% for friction coefficients of 0.428 and 0.2, respectively. The small differences between these three values and the fact that experimental model is regarded as a quite accurate representation of the plastic strain induced in the shear plane suggest that the actual plastic strain value is close to the calculated values.

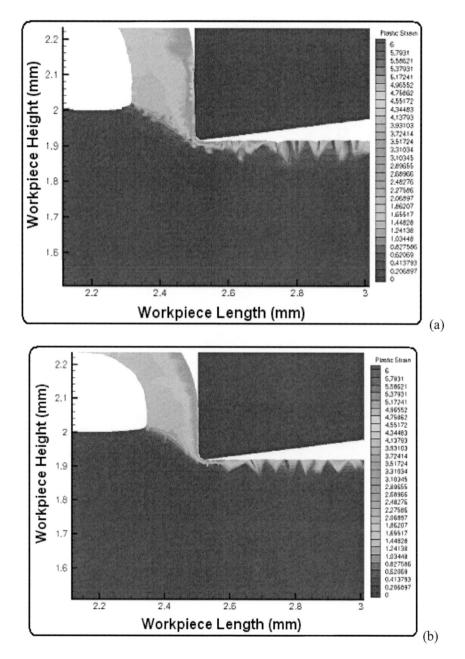

Figure 9. FEM simulation for plastic strain at the end of the cutting length: (a) friction coefficient of 0.428 and (b) friction coefficient of 0.2.

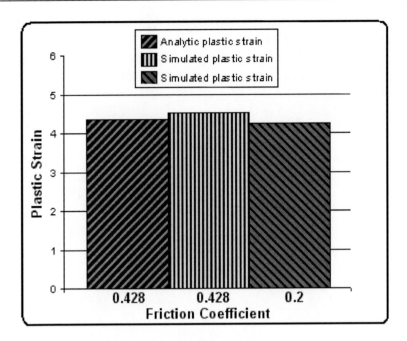

Figure 10. Plastic strain obtained analytically and by FEM simulations using distinct friction coefficients.

5. CONCLUSIONS

The following conclusions can be drawn from this work:

- The difference between the cutting and thrust forces values obtained experimentally and numerically was high, albeit best results were obtained simulating with a friction coefficient μ=0.2. The reason for that may be the influence of the cutting temperature in reducing the shear strength of the work material;
- The highest cutting temperature value obtained numerically presents a maximum difference of 12.7% (μ=0.428) compared with the value obtained analytically. An experimental investigation must be conducted in order to assess how close these values are from the actual cutting temperature;
- The results concerning the shear strain were similar (maximum difference of Δ=4.7%) and suggest that the actual plastic strain value in the primary shear plane is close to the calculated values.

ACKNOWLEDGMENTS

The authors wish to thank the Foundation for Science and Technology (FCT), Portugal, project POCTI/EME/61676/2004, for the use of the software licence Advantedge®.

REFERENCES

[1]   Kim, K. W., Lee, W. Y., Sin, H. C., A Finite-Element Analysis of Machining with the Tool Edge Considered, *Journal of Materials Processing Technology,* vol. 86, 45 – 55, 1999.

[2]   Mamalis, A. G., Branis, A. S., Manolakos, D. E., Modelling of Precison Hard Cutting Using Implicit Finite Element Methods, *Journal of Materials Processing Technology,* vol. 123, 464 – 475, 2002.

[3]   Qian, L., Mohammad, R. H., Effect on Cutting Force in Turning Hardened Tool Steels with Cubic Boron Nitride Inserts, *Journal of Materials Processing Technology,* vol. 191, 274 – 278, 2007.

[4]   Grzesik, W., Bartoszuk, M., Nieslony, P., Finite Difference Analysis of the Thermal Behaviour of Coated Tools in Orthogonal Cutting of Steels, *International Journal of Machine Tools & Manufacture,* vol. 44, 1451 – 1462, 2004.

[5]   Iqbal, S.A., Mativenga, P.T., Sheikh, M.A., Characterization of Machining of AISI 1045 Steel Over a Wide Range of Cutting Speeds. Part 1: investigation of contact phenomena, *Journal Engineering Manufacture,* vol.221, 909 – 916, 2007.

[6]   Umbrello, D., Filice, L., Rizzuti, S., Micari, f., On the Evaluation of the Global Heat Transfer Coefficient in Cutting, *International Journal of Machine Tools & Manufacture*, vol. 47, 1738-1743.

[7]   Özel, T., and Zeren, E., Numerical Modelling of Meso-Scale Finish Machining with Finite Edge Radius Tools, *Int. J. Machining and Machinability of Materials,* Vol. 2, n°. 3/4, 451 – 468, 2007.

[8]   Outeiro, J. C., Influence of Tool Sharpness on the Thermal and Mechanical Phenomena Generated during Machining Operations, *Int. J. Machining and Machinability of Materials,* Vol. 2, n°. 3/4, 413 – 432, 2007.

[9]   Boothroyd, G., Knight, W. A., *Fundamentals of Machining and Machine Tools,* 2ª ed., New York, Marcel Dekker, Inc., 542pg., 1989.

[10] Merchant, M. E., Mechanics of Metal Cutting Process I – orthogonal cutting and type 2 chip. *Journal of Applied Physics,* vol. 16, n°5, 267 – 275, 1945.

[11] Ozel, T., The Influence of Friction Models on Finite Element Simulations of Machining, International Journal of Machine Tools & Manufacture, vol. 46: 518–530, 2006.

[12] H. Bil, S.E. Kilic, A.E. Tekkaya, A Comparison of Orthogonal Cutting Data from Experiments with Three Different Finite Element Models, *Int. J. Mach. Tools Manufacture,* vol. 44, 933–944, 2004.

In: Micro and Nanomanufacturing Research
Editor: J. Paulo Davim
ISBN 978-1-61942-003-8
© 2012 Nova Science Publishers, Inc.

Chapter 5

THE EFFECT OF CUTTING SPEED ON CUTTING FORCES AND SURFACE FINISH WHEN MICRO-TURNING POLYAMIDES

Leonardo R. Silva[1,], A. M. Abrão[2], J. Paulo Davim[3]*

[1]Department of Materials Engineering, Federal Center for Technological Education of Minas Gerais - CEFET/MG, Av. Amazonas, 5253 - Nova Suíça, Belo Horizonte MG, CEP: 30.480-000, Brazil
[2]Department of Mechanical Engineering, University of Minas Gerais, Av. Antônio Carlos, 6627 - Pampulha, Belo Horizonte MG, CEP: 31.270-901, Brazil
[3]Department of Mechanical Engineering, University of Aveiro, Campus Santiago, 3810-193 Aveiro, Portugal

ABSTRACT

Composite materials are replacing conventional engineering metals and alloys in a variety of applications; nevertheless, machining of composite materials differs significantly in many aspects from machining of traditional metals and their alloys. Micro-machining aims the production of advanced components possessing small dimensions with high dimensional accuracy and acceptable surface integrity. The purpose of this chapter is to investigate the influence of cutting speed on micro-turning of polyamide with and without reinforcing (30% glass fiber) using polycrystalline diamond (PCD) and uncoated cemented carbide tools. The findings indicated that the addition of 30% glass fiber reinforcing significantly affected the performance of the tooling used in comparison with the material without reinforcing. The PCD tool provided lower force values for both work materials; however, the uncoated carbide tool gave similar surface finish results, thus offering a considerable cost reduction compared to the PCD compact.

---

* Corresponding author, E-mail: *lrsilva@feb.unesp.br*

INTRODUCTION

Most of the experimental research concerning micro-machining has been conducted on either conventional precision machine tools or prototype machine tools especially built for this purpose. Conventional machine tools used for precision machining have improved considerably with regard to motion accuracy, stiffness and capability. In general, micro-machining is performed on precision machine tools with power and dimensions typical of conventional machines, however, the required power and the work size are much smaller when micro-machining [1].

The value of many products can be substantially increased as their size and weight are reduced. The last decade has shown an ever-increasing interest in higher precision and miniaturization in a wide range of manufacturing activities. These growing trends have led to new requirements in machining, especially in micro-machining. With the trend towards miniaturization, micro-machining becomes increasingly relevant for the manufacture of micro-components. Many industrial branches require micro-components, for instance, telecommunication, biomedical and micro-intelligent technology. Micro-machining by shearing is capable of producing high dimensional and geometric accuracy, surface finish quality and sub-surface integrity at reasonably low cost. Thus, it should be the first choice amongst various manufacturing processes. Furthermore, conventional machining processes such as turning, milling and grinding are well established [2-4]. On the other hand, as the feed rate and depth of cut are reduced, special attention must be paid to the cutting edge preparation, otherwise the chip will not be generated owing to the side flow effect.

Therefore, the principal difference between conventional and micro-machining resides in the cutting mechanism. In general, the cutting mechanism in conventional machining is mainly shearing of the material ahead of the tool wedge, resulting in chip formation. In contrast, micro-machining relies on more complicated mechanisms depending on the degree of the size effect [1]. Additionally, in opposition to conventional cutting, micro-machining using depths of cut in the range of micrometers cannot neglect the effect of the tool nose radius. Considerable studies that consider the nose radius in orthogonal cutting have been conducted. When the depth of cut is larger than the nose radius, the effect of the latter may be ignored. However, in micro-machining the nose radius generally affects the cutting mechanism. In spite of that, few research works are reported on this subject matter [5-7]. *Kang et al.* [5] presented a cutting force model able to predict the cutting force in micro-end milling, in which the tool nose radius effect is taken into account. In order to validate the mathematical model, experimental tests were performed on aluminum with a 200μm diameter cutter.

Plastics are materials which have become of increasing importance, being employed in a wide range of applications in engineering products. Some of them are used to replace metals and other materials in applications that include gears, cams and bearings. Many of these components are made from injection-moulded engineering thermoplastics. Moreover, in recent years glass fiber reinforced plastics have caught increasing attention in applications such as load-bearing components, particularly for the aerospace industry. Among the properties which make this material of special interest, the following are highlighted: high specific strength, high specific modulus of elasticity, lightweight and good corrosion resistance. The applications require machined surfaces with high quality, including dimensional accuracy and surface integrity [8-9].

The machining of fiber reinforced plastics (FRPs) is quite distinct from that of metals and promotes many side effects such as accelerated tool wear rates, poor surface finish and subsurface layers damaged by cracks and delamination. Because FRPs contain at least two phases of materials which possess different mechanical properties, material removal mechanism is distinct from that of machining single-phased materials, such as metals. However, compared to the machining of metals, the investigations on that of FRPs are insufficient and limited to some special applications. Most of the FRP products are made to near-net-shape, albeit post-production removal of material in excess by means of machining is often carried out to meet dimensional requirements and assembly needs. Machining of FRP products is difficult due to their material discontinuity, inhomogenity and anisotropic nature. Glass fiber reinforced plastics are extremely abrasive, therefore, the selection of the most suitable cutting tool and machining parameters is important to the performance of the machining process [9-15].

The work material properties possess a significant influence on the success (or failure) of the machining operation. These properties and other characteristics of the work are summarized as the workpiece machinability, which indicates the relative ease with which a material can be machined using the appropriate tooling and cutting parameters. Several criteria are used to evaluate machinability, but the most important are tool life, cutting forces, power, specific cutting pressure and surface roughness [16-19].

The study on the cutting forces dynamics and surface roughness in any machining process is crucial for its proper planning and control, as well as for the optimization of the cutting conditions in order to minimize production costs and time. The cutting forces analysis plays a critical role when considering the various characteristics of a machining process, for instance, the dynamic stability, positioning accuracy of the tool with respect to the workpiece, roughness and form errors of the machined part [5, 20-21]. On the other hand, surface roughness is predominantly considered as the most important feature of engineering surfaces due to its influence on the performance of the machined component. Compared with conventional machining, however, the quality of micro-parts is much more difficult to be controlled and the quality of micro-components became a relevant aspect of micro-machining [20].

The principal aim of this chapter is to investigate the influence of cutting speed on cutting forces and surface roughness when micro-turning polyamide samples with and without reinforcing glass fibers using polycrystalline diamond and cemented carbide tools.

2. EXPERIMENTAL PROCEDURE

Micro-turning tests were conducted in order to study the influence of cutting speed (v_c) on machining forces (cutting, feed and radial forces) and surface roughness (R_a and R_t parameters). The workpiece materials used were polyamide with and without 30% glass fiber reinforcing (PA66-GF30 and PA66, respectively), produced by extrusion and supplied by ERTA® company.

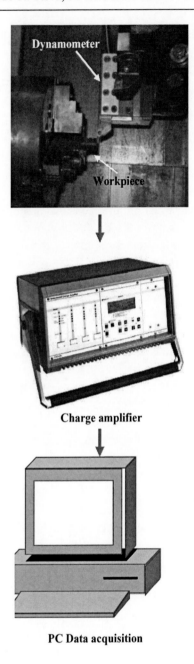

Figure 1. Machining forces measurement setup.

PA66 polyamide is an important thermoplastic widely used in injection moulded components, with the advantages associated to its low manufacturing cost. Typical applications include gears, cams and rolling bearing elements. PA66 is reported to possess superior wear resistance in comparison to other polymers due to its ability to form a thin and uniform transfer film while sliding against steel counterparts [22,23]. The mechanical and thermal properties of PA 66 polyamide and PA66-GF30 composite are presented in Table 1.

Table 1. Mechanical and thermal properties PA66 polyamide and PA66-GF30 composite by ERTA® Company

Property	PA 66	PA66-GF30
Elastic modulus (MPa)	1650	3200
Rockwell Hardness	M88	M76
Charpy impact resistance (KJ/m²)	Without fract.	≥50
Yield strength (MPa)	90	100
Melting temperature (°C)	255	255
Density (g/cm³)	1.14	1.29
Thermal conductivity at 23°C (W/K.m)	0.28	0.30
Coefficient of thermal expansion from 23 to 60°C (/K)	80×10^{-6}	50×10^{-6}
Coefficient of thermal expansion from 23 to 100°C (/K)	95×10^{-6}	60×10^{-6}

Table 2. Tools geometry

Tool	Rake angle γ_o (°)	Clearance angle α_o (°)	Cutting edge angle χ_r (°)	Cutting edge inclination angle λ_s (°)	Tool nose radius r_ε (mm)
PCD DCMW 11T3 04FPDC10	0	7	93	0	0.4
Uncoated ISO K15 carbide DCMW 11T3 04 H13A	0	7	93	0	0.4

Extruded bars with 20 mm diameter and 5mm long were turned with polycrystalline diamond - PCD insert (geometry code DCMW 11T3 04-FP) and plain cemented carbide insert ISO grade K15 (DCMW 11T3 04) tools, both with sharp cutting edges. The tools were mounted on a tool holder with geometry SDJCL 2020 K11, resulting in the cutting tool angles indicated in Table 2. Tool wear was negligible throughout the experimental program.

Dry turning tests were performed on a Kingsbury MHP 50 CNC lathe with 18 kW spindle power and maximum spindle speed of 4500 rpm. A Kistler® piezoelectric dynamometer model 9121 with a load amplifier connected to a computer was used for the acquisition of the cutting force (F_c), feed force (F_f) and radial force (F_r), as shown in Figure 1. Kistler Dynoware® software was used for data acquisition. The specific cutting pressure (K_s) was calculated as the ratio of the cutting force to the cross section area of the undeformed chip (feed rate x depth of cut), as indicated in Equation (1):

$$K_s = \frac{Fc}{S} \qquad (1)$$

Where:　　Ks = Specific cutting pressure (N/mm²)

F_c = Experimental cutting force (N)

S = Shear plane area (mm^2)

The surface roughness parameters R_a and R_t were assessed in accordance to ISO 4287/1 standard using a Hommeltester T1000 profilometer connected to a computer with Hommeltester Turbo-Datawin software. Average values were obtained using six roughness measurements.

The experimental work was carried out at constant values of feed rate (f=10 μm/rev) and depth of cut (a_p=100 μm). The cutting speed (v_c) values tested were: 35, 70, 140 and 210 m/min. Owing to the fact that the experimental work was conducted on a conventional CNC lathe, preliminary tests were performed in order to check the accuracy of the machine tool. These tests indicated a diameter repeatability of ±1μm (measured with a digital micrometer with 1μm resolution).

3. RESULTS AND DISCUSSION

The performance of PCD and K15 carbide tools when micro-turning PA66 polyamide and PA66-GF30 composite was evaluated in term of three component turning forces, specific cutting pressure and surface roughness (R_a and R_t).

Figure 2 and 3 illustrate typical results of forces evolution (F_c, F_f and F_r) along cutting time for each tool material for both work materials. In general, distinct patterns were observed for each workpiece material. Due to absence of tool wear, the forces remained stable during the tests. It can be noticed that, in general, the radial force presented the highest values, followed by the cutting force and finally by the feed force. The reason for that resides in the fact that the depth of cut of 100 μm is smaller that the tool nose radius (400 μm), therefore, the actual cutting edge angle becomes much smaller than χ_r=93° and the lower the cutting edge angle, the higher the radial force. Additionally, the forces recorded when turning the reinforced polyamide (Figure 2) were considerably lower compared to the polyamide without the glass fiber reinforcing, see Figure 3. This fact may be related to ductile behavior of the PA66 polyamide, as suggested by the properties presented in Table 1, which would cause the workpiece softening in the cutting zone. The presence of glass fibers would be responsible for the more brittle behavior of the reinforced polyamide, thus reducing the contact area and promoting lower forces. Another explanation for this behavior is the lower glass-transition temperature of the PA66 polyamide. The glass transition temperature is the temperature below which the physical properties of amorphous materials vary in a manner similar to those of a crystalline phase (glassy state), and above which amorphous materials behave like liquids. Therefore, glass-transition temperature is a kinetic phenomenon, in which amorphous polymers change their mechanical behavior from hard and brittle (at low temperatures) to rubbery (at high temperatures). Once cutting is finished, temperatures lowers and the molecules re-arrangement may take place, thus resulting in crystallization. The burrs observed at the end of cutting show evidence of melting followed by crystallization.

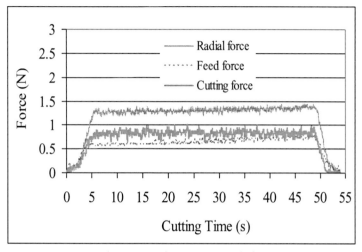

a) PCD tool at v_c = 35 m/min

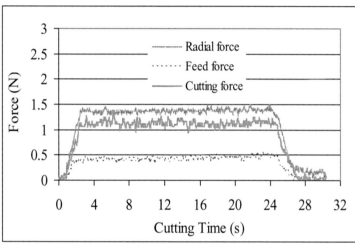

b) PCD tool at v_c = 70 m/min

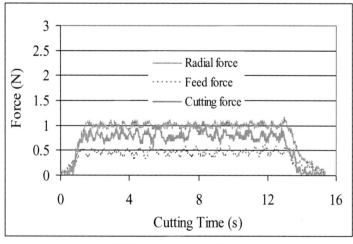

c) PCD tool at v_c = 140 m/min

Figure 2. (Continued).

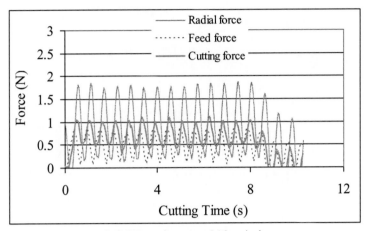

d) PCD tool at v_c = 210 m/min

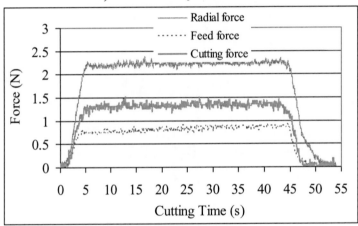

e) K15 carbide tool at v_c = 35 m/min

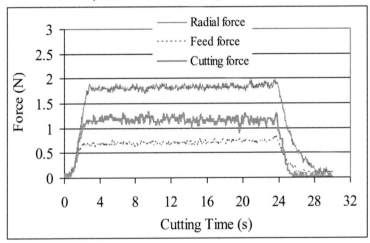

f) K15 carbide tool at v_c = 70 m/min

Figure 2. (Continued).

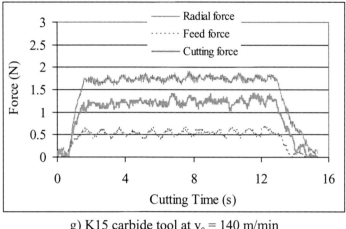

g) K15 carbide tool at v_c = 140 m/min

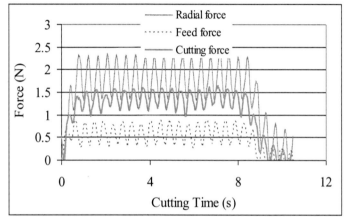

h) K15 carbide tool at v_c = 210 m/min

Figure 2. Turning forces evolution when cutting PA66-GF30 composite at f = 10 μm/rev and a_p=100 μm using PCD and K15 carbide tools.

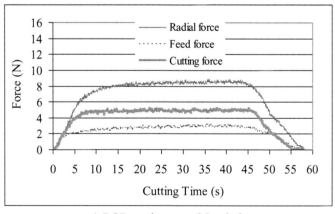

a) PCD tool at v_c = 35 m/min

Figure 3. (Continued).

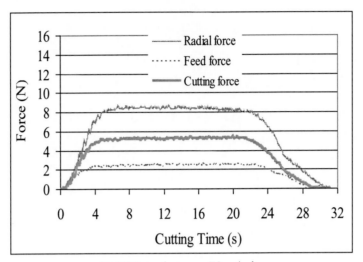

b) PCD tool at v_c = 70 m/min

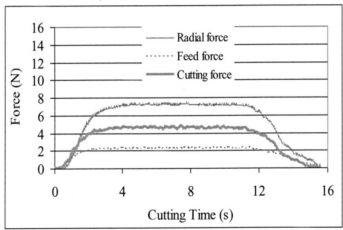

c) PCD tool at v_c = 140 m/min

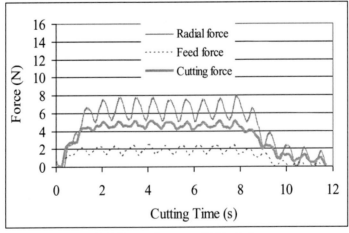

d) PCD tool at v_c = 210 m/min

Figure 3. (Continued).

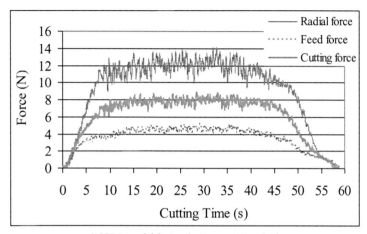

e) K15 carbide tool at v_c = 35 m/min

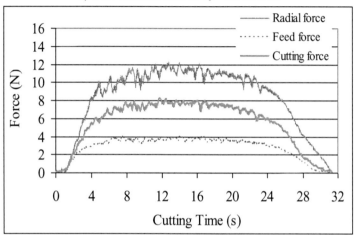

f) K15 carbide tool at v_c = 70 m/min

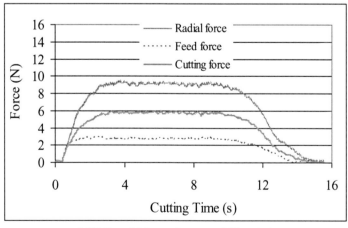

g) K15 carbide tool at v_c = 140 m/min

Figure 3. (Continued).

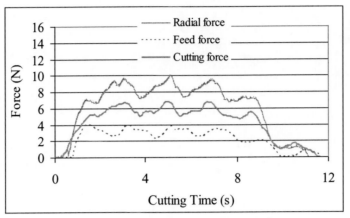

h) K15 carbide tool at v_c = 210 m/min

Figure 3. Turning forces evolution when cutting PA66 polyamide at f = 10 µm/rev and a_p=100µm using PCD and K15 carbide tools.

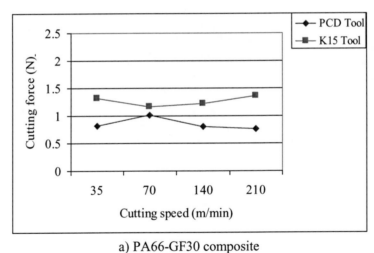

a) PA66-GF30 composite

b) PA66-GF30 composite

Figure 4. (Continued).

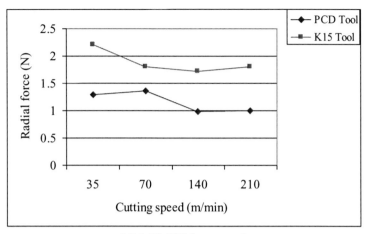

c) PA66-GF30 composite

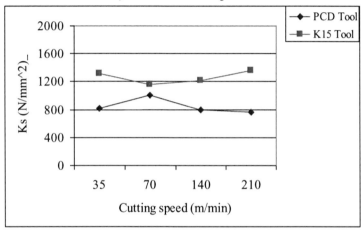

d) PA66-GF30 composite

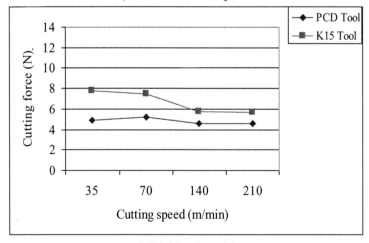

e) PA66 polyamide

Figure 4. (Continued).

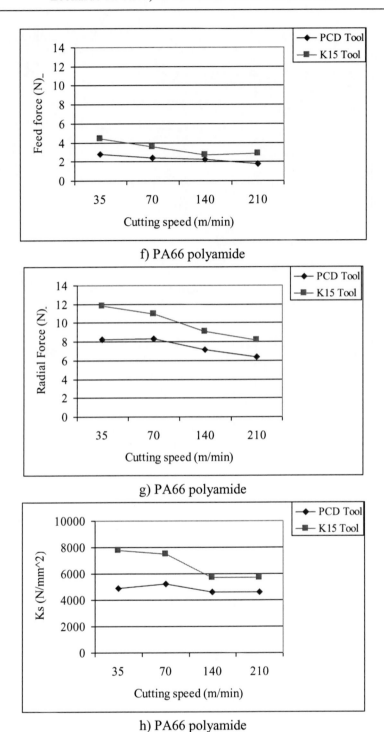

f) PA66 polyamide

g) PA66 polyamide

h) PA66 polyamide

Figure 4. Effect of cutting speed on turning forces and specific cutting pressure when machining PA66 polyamide and PA66-GF30 composite at f = 10 μm/rev and a_p=100 μm using PCD and K15 carbide tools.

The PCD tool presents the lowest values for the cutting, feed and radial forces compared with the K15 carbide tool for both workpiece materials, probably because of its lower surface roughness (polished rake face) associated to the low friction coefficient against the composite material. Comparing the four cutting speeds tested, it can be observed that the forces tend to decrease smoothly as cutting speed is increased. Chatter was observed when machining both materials at a cutting speed of 210 m/min (approximately 3700 rpm), as shown in Figures 2(d), 2(h), 3(d) and 3(h), suggesting that the machine tool is not sufficiently stiff to work above this rotational speed value.

Figure 4 presents the evolution of cutting, feed and radial forces and specific cutting pressure for both work material as a function of cutting speed when turning using PCD and K15 carbide tools. It can be noticed that the forces tend to either decrease slightly or to remain stable as cutting speed is elevated for both tool materials tested. Figures 4(d) and 4(h) show the influence of cutting speed on the specific cutting pressure (K_s) when micro-turning, respectively, PA66 polyamide and PA66-GF30 composite. It can be seen that in both cases the specific cutting pressure has a similar behavior. The PCD tool shows better performance under the four cutting speeds tested, presenting lower force and specific cutting pressure values for both workpiece materials.

Although many factors affect the surface texture of a machined part, the cutting parameters and tool geometry present a significant influence on workpiece roughness for a given machine tool and setup. Figure 5 shows the evolution of surface roughness as a function of cutting speed and tool material. Figures 5(a) and 5(b) present, respectively, the results concerning the R_a and R_t values for the PA66 polyamide, whereas Figures 5(c) and 5(b) show these findings related to the PA66-GF30 composite. In general, better surface finish is produced when machining the PA66-GF30 composite. The PCD tool provides considerably lower R_a and R_t values for both workpiece materials. The surface roughness produced was not significantly affected by cutting speed and similarly to the force results, the good performance of the PCD tool may be associated to the superior finish of its rake and clearance faces together with its lower friction coefficient against the material.

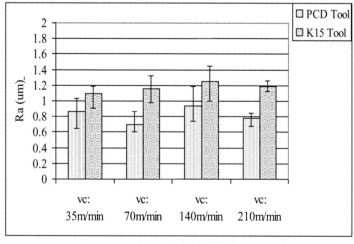

a) R_a - PA66-GF30 composite

Figure 5. (Continued).

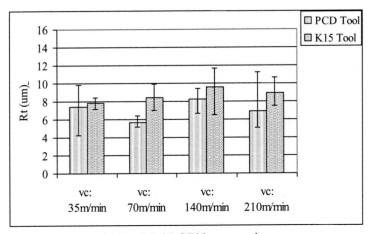

b) R_t - PA66-GF30 composite

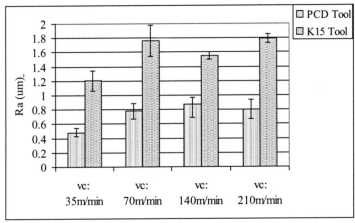

c) R_a - PA66 polyamide

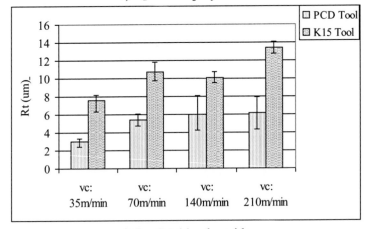

d) R_t - PA66 polyamide

Figure 5. Surface roughness values when turning PA66 polyamide (a and b) and PA66-GF30 composite (c and d) as a function of cutting speed and tool material.

4. CONCLUSION

Based on the experimental results presented, the following conclusions can be draw from micro-turning PA66 polyamide and PA66-GF30 glass fiber reinforced polyamide composite:

- The addition of 30% glass fiber reinforcing on the PA66 polyamide significantly affected the performance of the tooling used in comparison with the material without reinforcing.
- The radial force component presented highest values, followed by the cutting and feed forces, owing to the fact that the depth of cut is smaller than the tool nose radius, thus resulting in a smaller effective cutting edge angle. Similarly to conventional machining, the forces decreased as cutting speed increased.
- The specific cutting pressure either decreased slightly or remained unaltered as cutting speed was elevated. PA66 polyamide presented higher K_s values compared the PA66-GF30 composite.
- The surface roughness produced was not significantly affected by cutting speeds. Better surface finish was produced when turning the PA66 polyamide.
- In general, the polycrystalline diamond tool provided lower force values for both work materials; however, the K15 carbide tool gave similar surface finish results, thus offering a considerable cost reduction compared to the PCD compact.

ACKNOWLEDGMENTS

The authors would like to thank CAPES (Brazil) and FCT (Portugal) for funding this research project. They also acknowledge MSc. António Festas for his support during the experimental work.

REFERENCES

[1] Dornfeld, D., Min, S. and Takeuchi, Y. (2006). Recent Advances in Mechanical Micromachining, *Annals of the CIRP*, 55/2: 745-768.

[2] Fang, F. Z. and Liu, Y. C. (2004). On minimum exit-burr in micro cutting, *Journal of Micromechanics and Microengineering*, 14: 984-988.

[3] Azizur Rahman, M., Rahman, M., Senthil Kumar, A. and Lim, H. S. (2005). CNC microturning: an application to miniaturization, *International Journal of Machine Tools & Manufacture*, 45: 631-639.

[4] Fang, F. Z., Wu, H., Liu, X. D., Liu, Y. C. and Ng, S. T. (2003). Tool geometry study in micromachining, *Journal of Micromechanics and Microengineering*, 13: 726-731.

[5] Kang, I. S., Kim, J. S., Kim, Kang, J. H., Kang, M. C. and Seo, Y. W. (2007). A mechanistic model of cutting force in the micro end milling process, *Journal of Materials Processing Technology*, 187-188: 250-255.

[6]   Kim, K. W., Lee, W. Y. and Sin, H. (1999). A finite element analysis for the characteristics of temperature and stress in micro-machining considering the size effect, *International Journal of Machine Tools & Manufacture*, 39: 1507-1524.

[7]   Yuan, Z. J., Zhou, M. and Dong, S. (1996). Effect of diamond tool sharpness on minimum cutting thickness and cutting surface integrity in ultraprecision machining, *Journal of Materials Processing Technology*, 62: 327-330.

[8]   Apichartpattanasiri, S., Hay, J. N. and Kukureka, S. N. (2001). A study of the tribological behaviour of polyamide 66 with varying injection-moulding parameters, *Wear*, 251: 1557-1566.

[9]   Mohan, N. S., Kulkarni, S. M. and Ramachandra, A. (2007). Delamination analysis in drilling process of glass fiber reinforced plastic (GFRP) composite materials, *Journal of Materials Processing Technology*, 186: 265-271.

[10]   Wang, X. M. and Zhang, L. C. (2003). An experimental investigation into the orthogonal cutting of unidirectional fiber reinforced plastics, *International Journal of Machine Tools & Manufacture*, 43: 1015-1022.

[11]   Sang-Ook, A., Eun-Sang, L. and Sang-Lai, N. (1997). A study on the cutting characteristics of glass fiber reinforced plastics with respect to tool materials and geometries, *Journal of Materials Processing Technology*, 68: 60-67.

[12]   Gopala, G. V., Mahajan, P. and Bhatnagar, N. (2007). Micro-mechanical modeling of machining of FRP composites - Cutting force analysis, *Composites Science and Technology*, 67: 579-593.

[13]   Sonbaty, E., Khashaba, U. and Machaly, T. (2004). Factors affecting the machinability of GFR/epoxy composites, *Composite Structures*, 63: 329-338.

[14]   Rahman, M., Ramakrishna, S., Prakash, J. R. and Tan, D. C. (1999). Machinability study of carbon fiber reinforced composite, *Journal of Materials Processing Technology*, 89-90: 292-297.

[15]   Abrão, A. M., Faria, P. E., Campos Rubio, J. C., Reis, P. and Davim, J. P. (2007). Drilling of fiber reinforced plastics: A review, *Journal of Materials Processing Technology*, 186: 1-7.

[16]   Davim, J. P., Reis, P., Lapa, V. and António, C. (2003). Machinability study on polyetheretherketone (PEEK) unreinforced and reinforced (GF30) for applications in structural components, *Composite Structures*, 62: 67-73.

[17]   Davim, J. P. and Reis, P. (2004). Machinability study on composite (polyetheretherketone reinforced with 30% of glass fiber-PEEK GF30) using polycrystalline diamond (PCD) and cemented carbide (K20) tools, *Int. J. Adv. Manuf. Technol*, 23: 412-418.

[18]   Mata, F., Reis, P. and Davim, J. P. (2006). Physical cutting model of polyamide composites (PA66 GF30), Material Science Forum, 514-516: 643-647.

[19]   Davim, J. P. and Mata, F. A comparative evaluation of the turning of reinforced and unreinforced polyamide, *International Journal of Advanced Manufac. Technology* (in press).

[20]   Wang, W., Kweon, S. H., and Yang, S. H. (2005). A study on roughness of the micro-end-milled surface produced by a miniatured machine tool, *Journal of Materials Processing Technology*, 162-163: 702-708.

[21] Zaman, M. T., Senthil Kumar, A., Rahman, M. and Sreeram, S. (2006). A three-dimensional analytical cutting force model for micro end milling operation, *International Journal of Machine Tools & Manufacture*, 46: 353-366.

[22] Chen, Y. K., Modi, O. P., Mhay, A. S., Chrysanthou, A. and O'Sullivan, J. M. (2003). The effect of different metallic counterface materials and different surface treatments on the wear and friction of polyamide 66 and its composite in rolling-sliding contact, *Wear*, 255: 714-721.

[23] Chavarria, F. and Paul, D. R. (2004). Comparison of nanocomposites based on nylon 6 and nylon 66, *Polymer*, 45: 8501-8515.

In: Micro and Nanomanufacturing Research
Editor: J. Paulo Davim

ISBN 978-1-61942-003-8
© 2012 Nova Science Publishers, Inc.

Chapter 6

PULSED DROPLET MICROMACHINING OF ABRASIVE MATERIALS

M. J. Jackson[*]

Centre for Advanced Manufacturing, MET, College of Technology, Purdue University,
401 North Grant Street, West Lafayette, Indiana,
IN 47907-2021, US

ABSTRACT

There are many new manufacturing processes being developed for use at the micro and nanoscales. Many of these processes are simple adaptations of macroscale processes that have been scaled down to achieve tolerances and surface quality measures that are lacking at the macroscale. However, hybrid processes are also being developed that cross all length scale in order to produce products that cannot be manufactured with equipment that is simply scaled down. This paper describes a new method that uses the energy harnessed by impacting multiple droplets of liquid to remove material on the surface of microscale substrates. The process known as 'pulsed droplet micromachining' uses the useful properties of an attenuating Rayleigh wave to exploit surface imperfections that allows the bulk removal of material from the surface of a substrate and is described in this paper in terms of the underlying physical understanding of the process mechanism, the development of a dedicated machine tool to conduct such a process, and industrial data related to the expected material removal rates one should expect when employing such processes to machine materials at the microscale.

1. INTRODUCTION

To form a continuous drop of liquid during water jet machining, water is pumped to pressures in excess of 400 M Pa and is expelled through a sapphire nozzle that generates a

---

[*] Corresponding author, E-mail: jacksomj@purdue.edu

fine cutting stream. The stream of water is ejected at speeds in excess of 900 ms^{-1} and is used to cut materials such as paper, leather, plastics, cloth, fibre-glass, and composite materials [1]. The material removal rate of continuous water drop machining processes can be increased by mixing abrasive particles with the stream of water in the form of a suspension. The suspension of abrasive particles provides a five-fold increase in material removal rates compared to the abrasive water drop technique [1]. However, the effects of a continuous drop of water creating unacceptable kerf widths and taper of cut are well documented [1]. The continuous water drop system has not been adapted for material removal at the microscale, which would tend to encounter difficulties in maintaining shape integrity.

One way of eliminating these effects is to use a pulsed stream of liquid drops that create high pressures at the extremities of the impacting droplet that is powerful enough to erode material more effectively at the microscale than using the abrasive suspension water jet machining technique. Pulsed water drops that contact the surface of the material can be described using the theory of liquid impact [2]. There are various important implications from the theory of liquid impact. The first is that it is the initial stage of impact, which generates the extreme pressures that, leads to damage. This explains why thin plates are easily machined using a continuous stream of water. For thicker plates, a suspension of abrasive particles is usually mixed with a continuous stream of water in order to remove material below a critical thickness were energy is effectively dispersed without removing further material. The second is that the precise geometry in the contact region is critical in determining the duration of the high-pressure stage. For example, if the radius of curvature of a drop at contact with a plane surface is double that of a sphere of equivalent volume then the release time after impact is similarly doubled. The circumferential crack pattern that is produced after impact is generated by the interaction of the Rayleigh surface wave with pre-existing cracks in the surface of the material. This chapter illustrates how pulsed water drops can be used to machine selected materials at the microscale using a specially constructed pulsed water drop machining centre, and also explains how the theory of liquid impact can be used to predict the machining characteristics of elastically deformable brittle materials when subjected to pulsed water drops. The development of meso machine tools (mMTs) that are capable of delivering high velocity water droplets on a variety of materials is also described in depth.

2. PULSED DROPLET IMPACT

The impact of a liquid drop is divided into two regimes. The first is when the contact edge travels across the surface of the target at a velocity, V_c, which is greater than the shock wave velocity propagating into the water drop. The water behind the shock front, as a result of impact, is compressed as there are no free surfaces through which the pressure can be released. The shock-wave velocity into the water drop is reasonably well described, up to impact velocities of 1000 m s^{-1} using the following equation,

$$C = C_o + kV \tag{1}$$

Where C_o is the acoustic velocity, V is the impact velocity and k is approximately equal to two. Under the impact conditions considered here, the pressure exerted on the surface of a rigid target is known as the 'water-hammer pressure' P_c, which is described by the equation:

$$P_c = \rho C V \qquad (2)$$

Where ρ is the density of the water, 1000 kg m^{-3}, in this case. If the compressibility of the target is taken into consideration then the pressure in this initial regime is,

$$P_c = \frac{V \rho_1 \rho_2 C_1 C_2}{\rho_1 C_1 + \rho_2 C_2} \qquad (3)$$

Where ρ is the density and C is the shock wave velocity and the subscripts refer to the liquid and solid, respectively. The water-hammer pressure is not constant over the loaded region, which has high-pressure peaks, up to three times the contact pressure, at the edge of the contact zone at the point when the shock wave overtakes the contact edge. However, these edge pressures are of very short duration (usually a few nanoseconds) and can be ignored.

When the shock envelope overtakes the contact edge, a free surface is generated which allows the compressed region to release. The release waves propagate into the water drop from the free surfaces, thus reducing the pressure that is approximately the incompressible Bernoulli pressure, P_i, is given by,

$$P_i = \frac{\rho V^2}{2} \qquad (4)$$

For velocities considered in this study, the Bernoulli pressure is very much lower than the water-hammer pressure with the precise value dependent on the velocity, since the ratio of pressures is given by 2C/V. The radius over which high pressure acts can be calculated by examining the geometry of the impacting drop and considering the critical angle between the drop at the contact surface and the target. The radius of release, r, is the point at which the shock wave travels faster than the velocity at the edge of contact, V_c. The release radius is,

$$r = \frac{RV}{C} \qquad (5)$$

Where, R, is the radius of the impacting drop. For a four millimetres' diameter water drop impacting at 300ms^{-1}, the radius at which release occurs is approximately 300 μm. The time at which the release occurs can also be calculated using the geometry of the impacting drop. The time, after impact, τ, at which release first commences is,

$$\tau = \frac{RV}{2C^2} \qquad (6)$$

The release waves then propagate towards the centre of the compressed region. The total time for complete decompression is,

$$\tau_{rel} = \frac{3RV}{2C^2} \tag{7}$$

The duration of loading is very short. For example, the time for a four millimetres' diameter drop to release is 0.2 μs for a 300 m s^{-1} impact. From equation (5) and (7), it is clear that there are considerable changes in r and τ with changes in the drop diameter, R. There are various important implications from the theory of liquid impact. The first is that it is the initial stage of impact, which generates the extreme pressures that, leads to damage.

This explains why thin plates are easily machined using a continuous stream of water. For thicker plates, an abrasive is usually mixed with a continuous stream of water. The second is that the precise geometry in the contact region is critical in determining the duration of the high-pressure stage. For example, if the radius of curvature of a drop at contact with a plane surface is double that of a sphere of equivalent volume then τ is similarly doubled. The circumferential crack pattern that is produced after impact is generated by the interaction of the Rayleigh surface wave with pre-existing cracks in the surface of the material.

Liquid impact is conveniently studied by extruding a stream of water of known volume through a nozzle or drop. It is possible to relate the damage caused by a particular size of drop to that produced by the 'equivalent' spherical drop [3]. The point at which circumferential damage becomes visible at a particular velocity and is accompanied by material removal is known as the 'machining threshold velocity' (M.T.V.). At velocities higher than the M. T. V., material loss is increased leading to increased machining efficiency. The dynamic criterion for crack growth, and thus strength loss, is given by Steverding and Lehnigk [4] as,

$$\sigma^2\tau = \text{constant} \tag{8}$$

For liquid impact by water drops, equation (8) becomes:

$$\sigma^2\tau = \frac{3\rho^2}{2} RV^3 \tag{9}$$

Where σ is the impact, or water hammer, pressure and τ is the release time (refer to equation 7) [4]. This equation can be used to predict the machining threshold velocity for different sizes of water drops, R_1 and R_2, if the machining threshold velocity for one of the drop sizes is known. As $\sigma^2\tau$ is constant between the two drops, equation (9) can be used to find the water-drop radius ratio,

$$\frac{R_1}{R_2} = \left(\frac{V_2}{V_1}\right)^3 \tag{10}$$

Where, V_1, is the machining threshold velocity for crack extension for a water drop of radius, R_1. If a water drop is distorted in such a way that it has a profile equivalent to an effective increase in the radius of a factor of two, then the threshold velocity, V_2, is equal to $2^{-1/3} V_1$.

3. WATER DROPLET IMPACT

3.1. Circumferential Damage

The typical damage pattern induced on the surface of a brittle material shows an undamaged region in the centre and a clearly defined point, the release radius, at which damage is initiated. This can be explained by considering the decelerating contact edge [2]. When the contact velocity drops below that of the Rayleigh wave, the surface wave emerges and interacts with surface cracks. The cracks are distorted and tend to have a raised lip away from the impact centre [3,6]. As the Rayleigh wave moves away from the centre of impact, it is dispersed by interaction with surface cracks and distorts to a broader, less intense, pulse. The very sharp intense wave at the release radius extends many surface cracks by a short amount. As the wave propagates, the width of the wave increases and the magnitude tends to decrease due to attenuation and interaction with cracks.

The result is, at a greater radius, only the longer cracks are extended due to the greater stress intensity at the tip of the crack. At the edge of the visible damage, the wave has become so dispersed that it can only extend very large cracks, larger than are intrinsically seen in the material. When polishing scratches are present on the surface, they may be sufficiently large enough to extend. With single-crystal materials and diamond, the damage pattern consists of the opening of cleavage planes, and in the case of chemical-vapour deposited materials, the damage consists of reinforced ring cracks.

3.2. Lateral Jet Formations

When the shock wave moves to the free surface of the water drop and release commences, the water drop begins to spread across the surface of the material. The interaction of the water droplet with the target causes a high velocity sideways drop of fluid that has a velocity, V_j, which is faster than the impact velocity, V. Lateral jet formations exploit surface asperities, which arise from surface roughness or damage, introduced by the Rayleigh surface wave, resulting in material loss and further extension of cracks [2,6].

4. MACHINING THRESHOLD MODELLING

Machining threshold curves generated using the specially constructed machine tool are reproducible between samples of the same material. Figure 1 shows a typical impact damage crater caused by the impact of a single water droplet. Small circumferential cracks surround the site and each crack is modelled as a single crack with a critical crack length that is perpendicular to the impacting drop of liquid. The absolute machining threshold velocity (A.M.T.V.) of the sample material is related to the logarithm of the static fracture toughness, K_{IC}, of the material. However, the single-impact threshold velocity and the remaining part of the threshold curve, although reproducible, do not seem to have a simple relationship to a single fundamental material property. A computer programme was written that predicts the characteristic machining threshold velocity (M.T.V.) curve for a material with a particular crack size, fracture toughness, Young's modulus, and Poisson's ratio. Once developed it was possible to modify various material properties (such as critical crack size) thus allowing the possibility of investigating how the machining threshold velocity varies with changes in material properties.

4.1. Machining Threshold Model

The damage threshold model incorporates three sections. The first section contains a mathematical approximation of the damaging Rayleigh wave that relates to the quasi-static stress calculations and the stress intensity at the tip of the crack. The second section considers whether the crack being sampled is static, or opening, because an opening crack may have lower fracture toughness and, therefore, be easier to extend than static cracks. The third section considers the time dependency of the stress concentration at the crack tip, which can be considered as the response time to the passing wave, and relates strongly to the depth of the crack. The three components described are multiplied together, giving the dynamic stress intensity, K_{ID}. If the dynamic stress intensity is greater than the fracture toughness, K_{IC}, then the crack will extend.

In generating a threshold curve, up to three hundred impacts may be directed onto a single site. If the impact velocity is greater than the A.M.T.V. of the material then the crack will extend. It is believed that the machining threshold velocity, after three hundred impacts, will equate to the absolute machining threshold velocity of the material, i.e. if a crack starts to grow then it will be visible after 300 impacts. Therefore, a loop had to be generated in the computer programme that simulated a sequence of impacts, extending the crack after each impact until it had grown beyond a critical length when it became visible using an optical microscope.

The damage threshold model performs a theoretical impact and repeats this until the crack is greater than its critical length. The number of impacts required to extend the crack beyond its critical length and reach a length of 100 μm was recorded. If the visible length of the crack is not reached after 300 impacts, then it is assumed that the impact velocity is lower than the A.M.T.V. of the material. The data generated are then used to produce a theoretical machining threshold curve.

4.2. Quasi-static Stress Intensity

The quasi-static stress intensity is the intensity of the stress experienced at the crack tip assuming that the load is applied statically and across the whole length of the crack. However, it is not possible to provide a full stress analysis for a semi-elliptical crack in a varying stress field. The model uses the edge crack analysis by Hartranft and Sih [8], in which the quasi-static stress intensity is,

$$K_s = 2Y \left(\frac{C_L}{\pi} \right)^{1/2} \int_0^{C_L} \frac{\sigma(z)(1 + F(z/C_L))}{\sqrt{(C_L^2 - z^2)}} \, dz \tag{11}$$

Where Y is a dimensionless value which has a magnitude of approximately two for an edge crack, C_L is the crack length, z is distance into the material, with z=0 representing the impact surface. The integral was stored as a series of numerical values in an array that was interpolated depending on the impact conditions to be simulated. Hartranft and Sih [8] calculated the function F (z/CL) for the geometry of an edge crack as,

$$F(z/C_L) = (1 - (z/C_L)^2) \begin{bmatrix} 0.295 - 0.391\,(z/C_L)^2 + 0.769\,(z/C_L)^4 \\ -0.944\,(z/C_L)^6 + 0.509\,(z/C_L)^8 \end{bmatrix} \tag{12}$$

$F(z/C_L)$ is equal to 0.295 at the surface of the sample and zero at the crack tip. The function K_s has a discontinuity at the crack tip when $z = C_L$. For the purpose of the model, the upper limit of the integral was changed to $0.99C_L$, which approximates to a real crack due to blunting. The integral was evaluated numerically by using the rectangular method with integral steps of 1/10000 of the total crack length.

The function, $\sigma(z)$, as expressed by equation (11), refers to the stress wave induced by the Rayleigh surface wave over the complete length of the crack. Kolsky [9] stated that the wave function is,

$$\delta_1^6 - 8\delta_1^4 + (24 - 16\alpha_1^2)\delta_1^2 + (16\alpha_1^2 - 16) = 0 \tag{13}$$

Where δ_1 and α_1, are functions of Poisson's ratio such that,

$$\alpha_1^2 = \frac{1 - 2\upsilon}{2 - 2\upsilon} \tag{14}$$

$$\delta_1 = \frac{h}{\alpha_1} \tag{15}$$

Where h is a decay function of the Rayleigh wave [9]. Accounting for finite compressibility of, say, polycrystalline magnesium fluoride that has a Poisson's ratio of 0.18, equation (13) becomes,

$$\delta_1^6 - 8\delta_1^4 + (24 - 6.24)\delta_1^2 + (6.24 - 16) = 0 \tag{16}$$

$$4\delta_1^6 - 32\delta_1^4 + 71\delta_1^2 - 39 = 0 \tag{17}$$

The roots given by equation (17) are,

$$\delta_1 = \pm\, 0.91, \pm\, 1.6, \text{ and } \pm\, 2.15.$$

Hence, $\delta_1^2 = 0.828, 2.56, \text{ and } 4.62.$

Kolsky [9] stated that attenuation functions, f, q, and s, should be applied along the direction of propagation to describe the decaying nature of the passing wave. Therefore,

$$\frac{q}{f} = \sqrt{1 - \alpha_1^2 \delta_1^2} \tag{18}$$

$$\frac{s}{f} = \sqrt{1 - \delta_1^2} \tag{19}$$

Substituting the values of δ_1^2 and α_1^2, for polycrystalline MgF$_2$, gives the attenuation functions shown in Table 1. Lord Rayleigh [10] stated that, "the general theory of vibrations of stable systems forbids us to look for complex solutions of δ_1^2". Therefore, inserting real values of δ_1^2 into the decay functions expressed by Kolsky [9] gives $\frac{q}{f} = 0.822$ and

$\frac{s}{f} = 0.415$.

Table 1. Attenuation functions for a material with Poisson's ratio of 0.18 [2]

α_1^2	δ_1^2	q/f	s/f
0.39	0.828	0.822	0.415
0.39	2.56	0.045	complex solution
0.39	4.62	complex solution	complex solution

The rate at which the amplitude of the displacement along the direction of wave propagation is attenuated with depth depends on the attenuation factor,

$$e^{-qz} - 2qs \, (s^2 + f^2)^{-1} \, e^{-sz} \tag{20}$$

Substituting the values previously calculated for a material with a Poisson's ratio value of 0.18, gives,

$$\exp^{(-0.822fz)} - 0.582 \exp^{(-0.415fz)} \tag{21}$$

Here, the attenuation function, f, is the wave number of the stress pulse when used to calculate the Rayleigh wave function. For polycrystalline magnesium fluoride, the Rayleigh stress wave function is,

$$\sigma_r(z) = \sigma_0(\exp^{-0.822 \, fz} - 0.582\exp^{-0.415 \, fz}) \tag{22}$$

Where σ_0 is the magnitude of surface stress at impact, and again, f, is the wave number of the stress wave which is,

$$f(\lambda) = \frac{2\pi C^2}{3C_R RV} \tag{23}$$

Where, C, is the over-driven shock wave speed, C_R is the Rayleigh wave speed, R is the radius of the water drop, and V is the impact velocity. Stress wave functions were calculated for the materials investigated in this paper.

The Rayleigh wave contains both a shear and a longitudinal component. The wave is tensile at the surface and becomes compressive at a depth of approximately 40 % of its wavelength, which for a 200 m s^{-1} impact on zinc sulphide, occurs at approximately 200 μm. As the spatial decay of the Rayleigh wave is frequency dependent, it is necessary to determine the frequency for a given velocity.

The Rayleigh wave is a single pulse and does not have a single well-defined frequency. With the original simulation, it was decided to simply use the fundamental frequency to avoid having to perform a Fourier transform on the approximately shaped triangular pulse. At the release radius, Swain and Hagan [11] suggest that the peak height of the simplified triangular wave pulse be,

$$\sigma_{max} = \beta\rho CV \tag{24}$$

Where ρCV is the water-hammer pressure, and β is a function of the Poisson's ratio, υ, of the target material, being equal to,

$$\beta = \frac{1}{2}(1 - 2\upsilon) \tag{25}$$

The decay of the magnitude of the Rayleigh wave is proportional to $r^{-1/2}$. Therefore, the magnitude at any specified distance from the centre of impact may be calculated from the initial impact conditions and the properties of the target material. For the purpose of the model, the crack under examination was at its most stressed point, the release radius.

4.3. Dynamic Stress Intensity Factor

To model the interaction of a Rayleigh surface wave with a crack it is necessary to calculate the dynamic stress intensity factor at the crack tip. Freund [12] has analysed the case of a plane wave incident on a semi-infinite crack. The dynamic stress intensity factor has the following general form,

$$K_{ID} = k(v) . k(t) . K_s \tag{26}$$

Where $k(t)$ is the time-dependent coefficient of the dynamic stress intensity factor due to the shape of the stress wave, K_s is the quasi-static stress intensity factor for a crack of length, C_L, and $k(v)$ is a modifying coefficient to account for crack speed. The velocity of the opening crack must also be considered in the model.

A crack, which is opening with a low crack velocity, has high critical stress intensity than a crack with a high crack velocity (i.e. it is easier to keep the crack growing than it is to initiate growth). The damage threshold curve model relies upon a crack becoming visible when it reaches 100 μm in length; therefore, it is vital to know its velocity. A modifying function is incorporated in equation (26) to take account of the possibility of the crack opening. Freund [12] calculated the modifying function ($v = 0.25$) as:

$$k(v) = \frac{1}{\left(1 + \dfrac{v}{C_R - v}\right)\left(1 - 0.531\,\dfrac{v}{C_R}\right)^{1/2}} \tag{27}$$

Where v is the velocity of the crack. When the crack is static, k(v) is equal to one, and when the crack is opening up at the maximum theoretical velocity, the value of k(v) is zero, which is in agreement with the work of Broberg [13]. The current crack velocity (initially set at zero) is evaluated from the dependence of the crack velocity on the dynamic stress intensity factor and is given by,

$$v = v_{max}\left(1 - \left(\frac{K_{IC}}{K_{ID}}\right)^2\right) \tag{28}$$

Equation (28) is valid when the current crack velocity is greater than zero, where K_{ID} is the dynamic stress intensity, K_{IC} is the fracture toughness of the impacted material, and v_{max} is the maximum crack velocity [14]. Dulaney and Brace [15] and Berry [16], calculated the maximum crack velocity as,

$$v_{max} = \sqrt{\frac{2\pi E}{B\rho}}\left(1 - \frac{C_L}{a}\right) \tag{29}$$

Where B is a constant and C_L/a is the ratio of the crack length to sample thickness. Roberts and Wells [17] obtained a value for B, when $a >> C_L$, giving the maximum crack velocity as,

$$v_{max} = 0.38\sqrt{\frac{E}{\rho}} \tag{30}$$

Which is approximately equal to 0.6 C_R, where the Rayleigh wave velocity is the maximum theoretical crack velocity for fracture of brittle materials. Considering the time dependency of the dynamic stress intensity, for a time-dependent stress profile, σ(t), the stress wave may be considered as an incremental sum such that,

$$\delta\sigma(t) = \dot{\sigma}\,\delta t \tag{31}$$

The time-dependent coefficient of the dynamic stress intensity factor may then be evaluated using,

$$k(t) = \frac{2}{\pi} \int_0^t \dot{\sigma}(s)(t-s)^{1/2}\, ds \qquad\qquad (32)$$

This analysis is based on the geometry of a semi-infinite crack. For a finite crack, of length C_L, the result must be modified to account for stress wave reflection from the free surface (application of equation (32) would otherwise suggest that, for a finite length crack, the dynamic stress intensity factor tends to infinity as time tends to infinity, i.e. K_{ID} approaches ∞ as t approaches ∞).

In this case the time-dependent coefficient of the dynamic stress intensity factor can be expressed in the following form,

$$k(t) = f\left(\frac{vt}{C_L}\right) \qquad\qquad (33)$$

Where v is the velocity of the crack [18]. Sih [19] has evaluated the function shown in equation (33) numerically. The general form of a stress wave pulse implies that K_{ID} increases initially as $t^{1/2}$ reaches a maximum value that is 1.25 times greater than the quasi-static value.

It then decays in an oscillatory manner towards the quasi-static value as the time tends to infinity. This behaviour has been approximated in the present study by a dynamic stress intensity factor of the form,

$$K_{ID} = \frac{k(v)K_s}{\tau^{1/2}} \int_0^t \dot{\sigma}(s)(t-s)^{1/2}\, ds \qquad t < \tau \qquad\qquad (34)$$

4.4. Simulation of Liquid Droplet Micromachining

Liquid impact was simulated by modelling an approximately shaped triangular wave (the Rayleigh stress wave) moving radially away from the centre of impact. A computer programme was written [2, 6, 20] that simulated the extension of a surface crack until it appeared visible to the naked eye and resulted in material loss. The crack was situated immediately outside the release radius where the Rayleigh wave was developed.

The programme calculated the initial impact conditions such as equivalent water drop diameter based on the properties of the material, impact velocity, and the distance of the crack from the centre of impact. In order to increase the speed of computation, a set of pre-generated tables of quasi-static stress intensity factors were accessed using a simple linear interpolation routine to provide input for calculating the dynamic stress intensity factor. After setting the initial crack length as the critical crack length and its velocity at zero, a crack was excited by simulating the action of a passing Rayleigh wave over the length of the crack. An iterative procedure was established to simulate the passing wave over the crack up to three hundred times in order to establish the damage threshold of the target material.

Each iteration of the programme calculated the length of the crack after each wave pulse. Initially, the crack tip response time was calculated. The stress wave distribution, as a function of depth, was calculated and incremented with a pre-determined series of time steps. The time dependence of the stress wave, and its effect on the dynamic stress intensity factor was established by selecting the appropriate dynamic stress intensity factor that is dependent on the response characteristics of the material subjected to liquid impact.

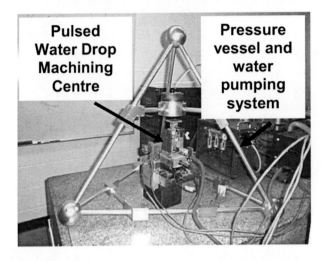

Figure 1. Pulsed water drop machining centre.

The programme also checked to see whether the crack was moving, or not, by comparing the dynamic stress intensity factor with the static fracture toughness of the material. The current crack velocity was calculated together with the new crack length. If the crack length exceeded 100 μm, then the number of iterations was determined for that particular impact velocity. For crack lengths less than 100 μm, the programme would re-iterate the routine to find the number of iterations required for the crack to grow to a length of 100 μm.

4.5. Machining Threshold Curves

Machining threshold curves were determined using the model described and by impacting specimens using the pulsed water drop machining apparatus. The accurate control of impact position, impact rate, and impact velocity means that a sample of material measuring approximately one-inch diameter can be used to generate a machining threshold curve. Up to twenty impacts sites are designated within the boundary of the specimen each with a different velocity assigned to it. These sites must be at least five millimetres apart from the edge so those cracks from different sites do not interact with each other. Figure 1 shows a schematic diagram of the pulsed water drop machining apparatus. The firing sequence for each water drop takes approximately 5 seconds to complete. This means that twelve pulses per minute can be ejected from the apparatus.

Each site is impacted once at its assigned velocity. The specimen is examined using an optical microscope at 100x magnification to inspect the occurrence of circumferential impact damage. Impact sites that remain undamaged are subjected to further impacts and re-examined using the optical microscope. The impact process is repeated until each site has been impacted three hundred times.

The characteristic machining threshold curve is a function of the number of impacts at particular velocities. The damage threshold point at three hundred impacts is assumed to be the absolute machining threshold velocity of the target material. At velocities below this point, circumferential damage is not developed. This is because the energy provided by liquid impact is not significant enough to extend cracks up to the visible limit. The materials used in this investigation were silicon carbide, alumina, and magnesium fluoride.

5. MICROMACHINING RESULTS

5.1. Silicon Carbide

The theoretical machining threshold curve for silicon carbide, shown in Figure 2, shows good agreement with the experimental machining threshold curve after a large number of impacts.

It should be noted that the fracture toughness and average crack size values used in the theoretical model were those values obtained from experiments conducted on samples used for determining threshold curve studies. However, the model became inaccurate when compared to the experimental data observed at the lower end of the damage threshold curve. This may be due to the method of observing machining threshold damage, and the fact that the first impact may excite a crack that is larger than the average crack size. The average crack size was determined to be 28 μm whilst the fracture toughness was found to be 2.94 MPa m$^{-\frac{1}{2}}$.

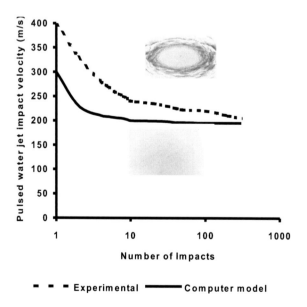

Figure 2. Computer modelled and experimental machining threshold curves for silicon carbide.

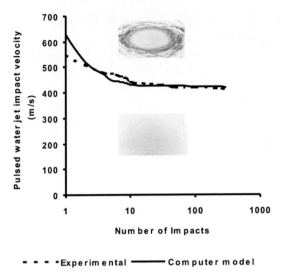

Figure 3. Computer modelled and experimental machining threshold curves for alumina.

5.2. Alumina

Alumina was selected to investigate whether the model could simulate a threshold curve for a tough material and one having a higher crack growth velocity. The fracture velocity used was 3700 m s^{-1} that ignores any crystalline orientation. As shown in Figure 3, there is good agreement with the machining threshold velocity using a fracture toughness of 2.5 MPa m$^{-\frac{1}{2}}$ and a crack size of 30 μm. The two experimental machining threshold curves shown are for samples with different surface roughness.

In this case, the surface roughness is incorporated into the computer programme by varying the crack size. However, the theoretical single-shot threshold velocity was higher than expected. The size of the minimum visible crack was investigated and was found to change the single-shot threshold velocity quite significantly with little variation in the A.M.T.V. Again, this may be explained by the fact that the first impact may excite a crack that is much greater than the crack size specified in the computer programme.

5.3. Magnesium Fluoride

Magnesium fluoride is a material that has a range of machining threshold velocities. A number of samples impacted suggested an average M.T.V. of 230 m s^{-1}. However, samples examined recently produced a machining threshold velocity of 190 m s^{-1}. The difference between the two samples may be due to differences in the way the materials were fabricated. If this is the case then the samples may have different fracture toughness and, as a result, different absolute machining threshold velocities (A.M.T.V.'s). To understand the difference a theoretical machining threshold curve was produced. The theoretical machining threshold curve produced accurate agreement with the latest samples examined. The predicted

M.T.V.(300 impacts) was 185 ± 5 m s^{-1} (Figure 4). The model, in this case, may be used to provide the user with a quality control tool to be used in the manufacture of such materials.

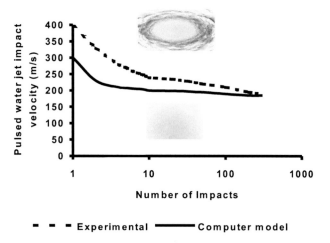

Figure 4. Computer modelled and experimental machining threshold curves for magnesium fluoride.

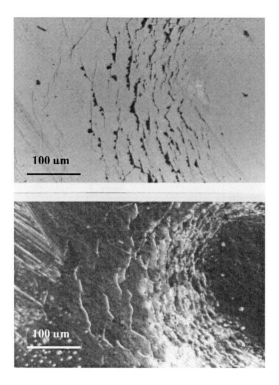

Figure 5. Edge of the impact crater showing localized damage caused by the Rayleigh surface wave.

6. MATERIAL REMOVAL RATES

The area of damage caused by liquid impact on polymeric surfaces has been investigated by Hand, Field and Townsend [20]. The measurement of impact erosion by water drops ejected from a converted air rifle was performed using a surface profilometer [20]. A model of damage was developed that incorporated an angle of impact between water drop and target. The equation derived for the area of damage was shown to be,

$$ A_d = K.\frac{\rho\pi r^2 V^3 \cos\theta}{C}.\left(1 + \frac{V^2 \sin^2\theta}{8C^2}\right) \tag{35} $$

Table 2. Material removal rates for materials machined using pulsed water drops

Material	Impact velocity (ms^{-1})	Material removal rate (mm^{3}min^{-1})
Silicon carbide	450	1.5
	500	3
	600	5
	700	7.2
	800	9
	900	11
	1000	14
Alumina	450	2
	500	4
	600	6
	700	8
	800	12
	900	15
	1000	18
Magnesium fluoride	250	6
	300	10
	400	14
	500	22
	600	30
	700	36
	800	43

Where K is a material constant, r is the radius of impact, C is the shock wave velocity, V is the impact velocity, ρ is the density of water, and θ is the impact angle.

Multiplying the depth of impact by the area of damage provides a measure of the removal of material by one single pulse of water at a particular velocity. In the present study, the author has directly measured a series of damage sites caused by water drop impacts and has presented this as a material removal rate. The impact sites were measured by traversing a surface profilometer across the impact sites (Figure 5) in a variety of different directions and depths in order to produce an impact profile of each crater. The maximum number of water pulses ejected from the pulsed water drop machining apparatus is twelve per minute, therefore, the damage per pulse is multiplied by twelve to achieve a volumetric material removal rate per minute.

Table 2 shows the measured material removal rates for silicon carbide, alumina, and magnesium fluoride materials at impact velocities in the range 250 to 1000 ms^{-1}. It should be noted that the lowest removal rates shown in Table 2 (at impact velocities in the range of 200 to 400 ms^{-1}) are similar to those obtained when micromachining using pulsed nanosecond and picosecond lasers. The highest removal rates obtained at impact velocities greater than 500 ms^{-1} are comparable to micromachining methods that use traditional cutting tools.

7. DESIGN OF MACHINE TOOLS FOR LIQUID DROPLET MICROMACHINING

The problem with existing machine tool structures is the amount of vibration that is transmitted through the spindle or nozzle, which affects the quality of surface finish and the dimensional accuracy imparted to the workpiece being machined. Owing to the way the spindle is mounted at the end of a cantilevered structure, low resonant frequencies can occur that are easily excited.

In addition, the amplitude of oscillation is more pronounced due to the geometry of the spindle mounting. An alternative approach is to design a vibration suppressing machine tool structure. When vibrations travel through a tetrahedral structure, they are canceled out or minimized due to the interference between the vibrating waves as they travel through the loops of the structure. The ability to dampen out vibrations is needed because if the spindle oscillates during machining, an increase in the depth of cut, or a variation in the plane of impact, will occur thus reducing the quality of surface finish, or dimensional accuracy of the machined part will be reduced significantly.

Modal analysis experiments were performed to investigate the structural response of the structure. Modal analysis experiments consisted of measuring the natural frequencies of the structure and performing frequency response functions (F.R.F.) to determine the mode shapes of the structure. In addition, a finite element model (F.E.A.) model was constructed to compare to the experimental data, which also may be used for modeling any alterations to the design.

8. ANALYSIS OF SPACE FRAME

The tetrahedral frame was initially analyzed from a numerical viewpoint using a closed-form solution and a numerical solution using finite element analysis.

8.1. Finite Element Model

Modal analysis of the tetrahedral structure using the finite element method was performed to obtain the natural frequencies and the mode shapes within the range of 0-8500 Hz, to compare to experimentally determined mode shapes. Modal analysis simulation was performed using the finite element software package ANSYS 6.1. Model preparation was the first step in analyzing the modes of the tetrahedral structure. This step involved creating a beam model of the structural members. The six bars that link the spheres and the reinforcement connections, which tie together the spindle sub-frame and the reinforcement bars were modeled using (ANSYS beam 188 elements), which have three translational degrees of freedom U_x, U_y, and, U_z at each node and three rotational degrees of freedom θ_x, θ_y and θ_z. The three rotational degrees of freedom were needed to accurately simulate the boundary conditions at the vertices of the structure. The finite element model, shown in Figure 6 consists of 115 elements and 513 nodes. The material properties of cold rolled steel were used in the modal analysis.

Each of the beam elements used enabled a geometric cross-section to be assigned. Each of the structural beams was given a circular cross-section of 0.75 inches' diameter. The spindle holder was modeled by using a 3.5-inch outer diameter and a 0.70 inch inner diameter beam. This allowed the spindle holder to rotate and bend in a smooth manner. To simulate the spheres located at each of the vertices of the structure, a mass element (ANSYS mass 21) was used. The actual spheres of the structure were weighed and mass moments of inertia were calculated, and then put into the mass element model. Beam elements were chosen over solid elements to reduce the computation time required to solve the problem.

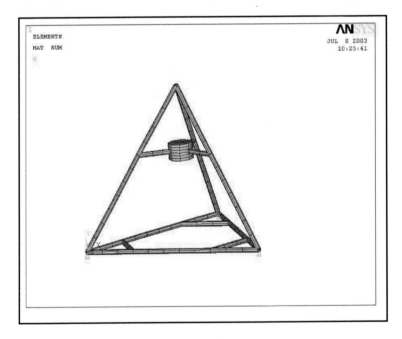

Figure 6. Finite element model of the tetrahedral space frame.

8.2. Closed-form Solution Model

Sample calculations were performed to approximate the dynamic response of the tetrahedral structure. The purpose of these calculations is to obtain a continuous model of the structure instead of a finite element approximation. The structure was modeled as four spheres at each of the vertices of the tetrahedron, with springs simulating the structural links between them. Equation 36 was the equation used to generate a mathematical model of the structure.

$$[M] * \ddot{X} + [K] * X = 0 \tag{36}$$

Where, $[M]$ is the matrix of masses for each sphere, $\ddot{X}$ is the acceleration of each sphere, $[K]$ is the stiffness matrix for all of the structural links, and X is the displacement of each sphere. Equation 37 was used to model the stiffness (K) of each connecting rod (axial displacements are considered in this formulation to decrease the complexity of the solution),

$$K = \frac{A * E}{L} \tag{37}$$

Where A is the cross-sectional area, E is Young's modulus of elasticity, and l is the length of the beam. Since this structure was modeled as a 9 degree-of-freedom (d.o.f.) system, the methods listed by Inman [21] were used. This method assumes that each of the d.o.f.'s can be modeled by the superposition of several single d.o.f. systems. The structure is a three-dimensional structure, where each equation had to be related to a global coordinate system similar to the methods used in finite element formulations. There were three degrees of freedom for the top sphere and two degrees of freedom for the base spheres, which led to 9 possible natural frequencies. Damping was not considered in the mathematical modeling of this structure since it would create more difficulty in solving the equations.

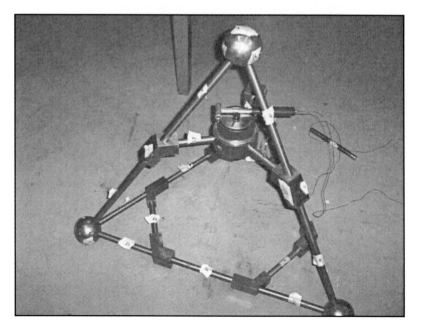

Figure 7. Tetrahedral structure showing marked points of vibration measurement and the impact hammer used to excite the structure.

9. MODE SHAPES OF TETRAHEDRAL STRUCTURES

The impact hammer test has become a widely used device for determining mode shapes. The peak impact force is nearly proportional to the mass of the head of the hammer and its impact velocity. The load cell in the head of the hammer provides a measure of the impact force. This data is used to compute the frequency response function (F.R.F.). The use of an impact hammer avoids the mass-loading problem and is much faster to use than a shaker. An impact hammer consists of a hammer with a force transducer built into the head of the hammer. The hammer is used to impart an impact to the structure at designated points of the structure and excite a broad range of frequencies. The impact event is supposed to approximate to a Dirac-delta function [22].

9.1. Experimental Method

The tetrahedral structure was placed on a granite table in order to gain accelerometer measurements, thus the structure was allowed to freely move longitudinally and transversely across the table. The roving accelerometer approach was used for all of the measurements. The centre of the spindle frame was used as the excitation point for the structure. The accelerometer was placed at various points of interest about the structure. Figure 7 shows the experimental structure and the impact hammer used to excite the structure.

9.2. Experimental Procedure

The data acquisition system was set up to take data at a sampling frequency, F_s, of 17000 Hz for 8192 points with a delay of 100 points. The voltage range on both channels was set to +\- 5 volts. Data was acquired in the time domain by averaging 8 ensembles and storing the data in binary format. This data was used to find the natural frequencies of the structure and their corresponding mode shapes. While applying the roving accelerometer technique, the structure was excited in the centre of the spindle sub-frame and data was acquired at points 1-28. Before the time domain data was stored, it was filtered to remove any aliasing that might have occurred from under-sampling. This was accomplished by installing an analog filter between the power supply and the P.C. The frequency was set at 8500 Hz, which corresponds to the Nyquist frequency of the measured data. After the data was recorded, it was translated into a binary file.

The method used on the F.R.F. data of a multi-degree-of-freedom structure is the single-degree-of-freedom-curve-fit (S.D.O.F.). In this method the frequency response function for the compliance is sectioned off into frequency ranges bracketing each successive peak. Each peak is analyzed by assuming that it is the F.R.F. of a single-degree-of-freedom system. This assumes that in the vicinity of resonance the F.R.F. is dominated by that single mode. Once the frequency response function (F.R.F.) is completed for the chosen data points of a structure, it is then appropriate to compute the natural frequencies, damping ratios and modal amplitudes with each resonant peak. The damping ratio associated with each peak is assumed to be the modal damping ratio, Zeta (ζ). The modal damping ratio Zeta is related to the frequencies corresponding to Equation 3.

$$\left| H(\omega_a) \right| = \left| H(\omega_b) \right| = \frac{\left| H(\omega_d) \right|}{\sqrt{2}} \tag{38}$$

And $\omega_b - \omega_a = 2\zeta\omega_d$, so that

$$\zeta = \frac{\omega_b - \omega_a}{2\omega_d} \tag{39}$$

W_d is the damped natural frequency at resonance such that ω_a and ω_b satisfy Equation 38. The condition of Equation 3 is termed the 3 dB down point. Both the natural frequency and the damping ratio Zeta may be found using this method. Once the values of ω_a and ω_b are determined, then ζ is found for the structure at the prescribed frequency (Equation 39). This method was used in the software to experimentally determine the damping and mode shapes.

9.3. Experimental Analysis

Using the measured data obtained from Me-Scope software, a model was constructed and the data was used to find structural damping and mode shapes. At first it was thought that the data was too low since the operating frequencies of the spindle are above 4500 Hz. However the operating frequencies of the spindle could excite lower frequencies while machining. Therefore, this data is useful if the structure is excited at these frequencies by some other means, such as localized impacts the structure might experience during a machining operation. This is shown in the following series of illustrations at the chosen frequencies (Figures 8 –10). The measured data for each node was adjusted such that the axis of orientation corresponded with the orientation of the accelerometer.

The measured data compared accurately with the finite element results. It was found that the placement of the centre of the spindle proved to be a point inside the structure that experienced minimal oscillations. It appeared that the structure was kinematically balanced such that different parts of the structure had oscillations that were out of phase with other parts. The results from finite element compare favorably. The tetrahedral structure was analyzed in its working orientation. The results are tabulated in Table 3. Not all of the results are listed, only those of interest. The first column is the measured natural frequency, followed by the finite element generated natural frequency in the second column. The measured data mode shape is given first, followed by a corresponding finite element generated mode shape. As the frequency is increased, the results from the finite element model seem to diverge from the measured mode shapes.

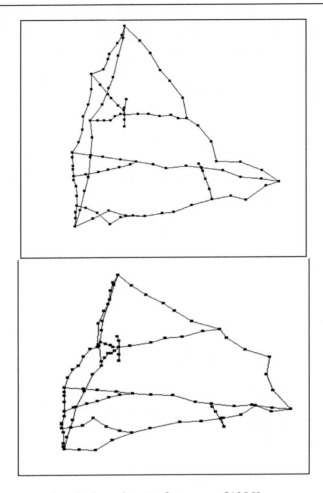

Figure 8. Me-Scope measured mode shape data at a frequency of 125 Hz.

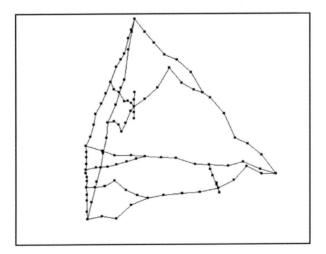

Figure 9. (Continued).

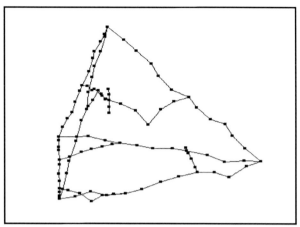

Figure 9. Me-Scope measured mode shape data at a frequency of 232 Hz.

Table 3. Comparison between experimental results and finite element calculations

Experimental Data (Me-Scope software)	Finite Element Results (ANSYS software)	% Difference in Results
125	125	0%
203	200	1%
401	407	-1%
534	535	0%
601	600	0%
1070	1085	-1%
1820	1794	1%

It is thought that as oscillation modes increase they tend to depart from Bernoulli beam theory upon which the finite element generated results depend. For most of the natural frequencies, the amount of oscillation of the spindle is small, or approximately zero, which is preferred since the amount of spindle oscillation from equilibrium is translated directly to the machined workpiece.

The results from ANSYS above 1794 Hz did not coincide with what was measured therefore no comparison was made. However, measured frequencies above 1820 Hz are shown because they are useful for future design revisions to the structure. Axial responses, as well as transverse responses, from the measured data were used to compare to the finite element results. Torsional data was ignored since it was not recorded using the accelerometer and the Me-Scope measurement software. It can be seen from the percent difference that the results from ANSYS have a natural frequency that resembles the measured results. However, they do not converge exactly instead the results oscillate about the measured data. The measured mode shape data using Me-Scope software at a frequency of 125 Hz shows an axial deflection for the spindle frame. However, the spindle itself remains stationary. The ANSYS model shows bending in the spindle sub-frame. The finite element models show the occurrence of bending modes. The measured mode shape at 232 Hz illustrates how the structure cancels out oscillations that are transmitted through the spindle. It is apparent from the measured mode shape as well as the finite element model, how various structural members are out of phase, which prevents any displacement of the spindle from its equilibrium position thus achieving a preferred effect for micromachining.

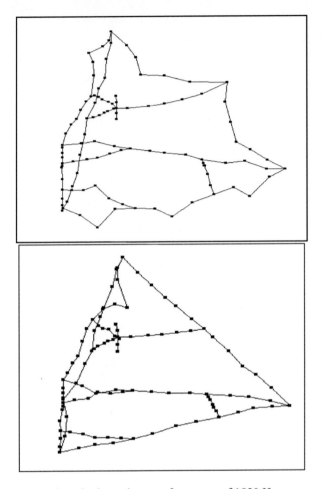

Figure 10. Me-Scope measured mode shape data at a frequency of 1820 Hz.

The measured data vaguely coincides with the finite element model once the frequencies reach approximately 1800 Hz, as illustrated from the images from Me-Scope at 1820 Hz and the finite element results at 1794 Hz. For this reason the finite element results have been omitted above 1820 Hz. This may be due to inadequate modeling of the structural connections, but most likely due to Bernoulli beam theory not being applicable at these frequencies.

The only characteristic that is common to both of the models is the restricted oscillation of the spindle. There is virtually zero oscillation in the spindle at most of the measured frequencies, this is accompanied by the finite element model as well. The reason for omitting results above 4460 Hz is because the F.R.F. from the measured data was not clear, thereby resembling noise, which is not useful for an adequate conclusion to be made. This is because the impact hammer method of exciting a structure is limited to approximately 4000 Hz. However, the frequencies used in this design exercise are those commonly encountered during micromachining processes. It appears that further improvements can be made by using passive damping systems on subsequent designs of meso machine tools (mMT) used for liquid droplet micromachining processes.

10. DISCUSSION AND CONCLUSIONS

The computer model developed for pulsed water drop micromachining simulates impacts from a 0.8 millimetres' diameter nozzle and determines the extent of crack growth. If an estimate of 'visible' crack size is made, then the machining threshold velocity for a given liquid impact velocity can be predicted. The simple machining threshold model of liquid impact produced accurate M.T.V.'s (300 impacts) with good agreement with experimentally obtained values. The lower impact end of the damage threshold curve was the most difficult to model as it depends on the size of the largest crack and the minimum crack size that is detectable by eye using an optical microscope. This was apparent when an opaque material was investigated.

With silicon, the model underestimated the experimental single impact threshold velocity. The model showed that the M.T.V. (300 impacts) is a reliable estimate of the A.M.T.V. The variation in the absolute machining threshold velocity with crack size was investigated and was seen to increase when the initial crack length was reduced. When the crack became longer, the A.M.T.V. became almost independent of the length of the crack. This is an agreement with experimentally obtained data, where the change in the M.T.V. (300 impacts) with surface roughness is lower than the effect on fracture stress. This is due to the brevity of the Rayleigh wave pulse both spatially and temporally, and the fact that the damaging Rayleigh wave decreases rapidly with depth. When breaking samples, the whole piece is quasi-statically loaded and, therefore, larger cracks are exploited in reducing strength and resulting in a loss of material. Pulsed water drop micro machining appears to be a new method to add to the newly developing field of environmentally conscious manufacturing processes.

It should be pointed out that the pulsed water drop machining process has not been compared to the traditional continuous water drop machining processes. Therefore, one cannot compare the effectiveness of the new method compared to these techniques other than in terms of the quality of cut and material removal rates.

The finite element model predictions of the pulsed water drop machining centre compare well with measured data at low frequencies. Owing to this fact, the finite element model may be used for future design improvements to the structure. It can be seen from the experimental and the measurement results that multiple constraints on the spindle enhance the ability of the structure to resist excitation. One possible reason for the structure's oscillation is probably due to the lack of passive damping. Therefore, it is recommended that improvements be made to improve passive damping of oscillations. The results presented show that modifications can be made to a seemingly stiff machine tool structure. Improvements made to enhance passive damping through the use of different materials that will enable the tetrahedral framework to be adapted to produce a meso machine tool (mMT) structure that will possibly allow pulsed water drop micromachining processes to become mass manufacturing processes.

REFERENCES

[1]   Hashish, M, and Hilleke, M., (1999), *Water Drop Machining of Composites and Ceramics,* in Machining of Ceramics and Composites, Chapter 13, p.p. 427-482, Marcel Dekker, New York.

[2]   Jackson, M. J. and Field, J. E., (2000) *Modelling Liquid Impact Fracture Thresholds in Brittle Materials,* Journal of the Institute of Materials, Minerals, and Mining - British Ceramic Transactions , 99, 1-13.

[3]   Bowden, F.P. and Brunton, J.H, (1961), *The deformation of solids by liquid impact at supersonic speeds,* Proc. Roy. Soc. Lond., A263, 433-450.

[4]   Steverding, B., and Lehnigk, S.H., (1969), *Dynamic thresholds for crack propagation,* Int. J. Fract. Mech., 5, 369-370.

[5]   Miller, G.F., and Pursey, H., (1956), *On the partition of energy between elastic waves in a semi-infinite solid,* Proc. Roy. Soc. Lond., A233, 55-69.

[6]   Jackson, M.J., and Field, J.E., (1999), *Liquid impact erosion of single-crystal magnesium oxide,* Wear, 233-235, 39-50.

[7]   Obara, T., Bourne, N.K., and Field, J.E, (1995), *Liquid drop impact on liquid and solid surfaces, Wear*, 186-187, 338-344.

[8]   Hartranft, R.J., and Sih G.C. (1973): in Methods of analysis and Solutions of crack problems (ed. G.C. Sih), 179-238, Noordhoff International Publishing.

[9]   Kolsky, H. (1953), *"Stress waves in solids"*, Clarendon Press, Oxford, England.

[10]   Lord Rayleigh (1885), *On waves propagated along the plane surface of an elastic solid, Proc. Lond. Math. Soc., 17, 4-11.*

[11]   Swain, M.V., and Hagan, J.T (1980), *Rayleigh wave interaction with, and the extension of, microcracks,* J. Mat. Sci., 15, 387-404.

[12]   Freund, L.B. (1972), J. Mech. Phys. Solids, 20, 129-140.

[13]   Broberg, K.B. (1960), *The propagation of a brittle crack,* Arkiv. Fur Fysik., 18, 159-192.

[14]   Kerkhoff, F., and Richter, H. (1969): in 2nd Int. Conf. "Fracture", 463-473, Brighton, England.

[15]   Dulaney, E.N., and Brace, W.F. *(1960),* J. Appl. Phys., 31, 2233-2236.

[16]   Berry, J.P. (1960), J. Mech. Phys. Solids, 8, 194-216.

[17]   Roberts, D.K., and Wells, A.A. (1954), Engineering, 178, 820-821.

[18]   Evans, A.G., in "Treatise on Materials Science and Technology", Erosion (ed. C.M. Preece), 1979, 16, 1-67, Academic Press, New York.

[19]   Sih, G.C.: "Handbook of stress intensity factors", 1973, Lehigh University Press, Pennsylvania, US.

[20]   Hand, R. J., Field, J. E., and Townsend, D., (1991), *The use of liquid water drops to simulate angled drop impact,* J. Appl. Phys., 70, 7111-7118.

[21]   Inman, Daniel J., *Engineering Vibration,* Prentice Hall, Upper Saddle River, New Jersey, 2001.

[22]   Cook, Robert D., *Finite Element Modeling For Stress Analysis,* John Wiley & Sons Inc., New York, 1995.

In: Micro and Nanomanufacturing Research   ISBN 978-1-61942-003-8
Editor: J. Paulo Davim   © 2012 Nova Science Publishers, Inc.

Chapter 7

SOME ASPECTS OF NON-CONVENTIONAL MICRO MACHINING TECHNOLOGY: AN OVERVIEW

Taha Ali El-Taweel[*]

Department of Production Engineering and Mechanical Design, Faculty of Engineering,
Menoufiya University, Shebin El-Kom, Egypt

ABSTRACT

The miniaturization of parts and components plays an important role in today's technology, enabling the design and production of new and highly sophisticated technology in various industrial fields, such as automotive, medical, biochemistry, telecommunications and other high-tech industries. Non-conventional machining processes are getting their importance due to some of specific advantages that can be exploited during micro machining operations. Out of those available non-conventional techniques, the most dominating manufacturing methods are micro electrochemical machining (micro ECM), micro electrodischarge machining (micro EDM), micro laser machining (micro LM), and micro ultrasonic machining (micro USM). In this paper, a brief overview on the basic principles governing the performance of micro ECM, micro EDM, micro LM and micro USM are discussed. Various aspects of micro machining utilizing those methods are also thoroughly reviewed. "Through-mask and maskless" micro electrochemical machining, are discussed with respect to material removal rate, shape evolution, tooling and control. Also, various methods of micro EDM are presented. Furthermore, micro LM, which can be categorized into mask projection technique and direct writing technique, is discussed. Moreover, micro USM is reviewed regarding to its tooling. Finally, successful applications of these non-conventional micro-machining techniques are described.

---

[*] Corresponding author, E-mail: tahaeltaweel@yahoo.com

1. INTRODUCTION

Micro machining is the most basic technology for the production of miniaturized parts and components for very small machines such as micro robots, capsules inserted into human body for medical treatment, micro-motors, micro-sensors, etc. (Corbett et al., 2000; D'Arrigoa et al. 2002). The term micro machining refers to material removal of very small dimensions that range from several microns to one millimeter. However, as a technical term, it also means that a smaller amount of machining which cannot be achieved directly by conventional techniques. Non-conventional machining processes are getting their importance due to some of specific advantages that can be exploited during micro machining operations. Out of those available non-conventional techniques, the most dominating manufacturing methods are micro electrochemical machining (micro ECM), micro electrodischarge machining (micro EDM), micro laser machining (micro LM), and micro ultrasonic machining (micro USM). These processes are now receiving much greater attention in the electronics and other high-tech industries for the fabrication of micro components (Rajurkar et al., 2006; Pecholt et al., in press; Kurita et al., 2006; Zhang et al., 2007).

Masuzawa and Tanshoff (1997) have drawn attention to the need for characterization of micro machining and in particular to means for direct determination of the shape of its product. Two basic groups of micro machining processes were defined. The first one utilizes fixed controlled tools, which can specify the profiles of three-dimensional shapes, by well-defined tool surface and path. This method removes material by small amount of tens of nm, which is acceptable for many applications of micro machining. For finer precision, especially to atomic levels, the second group of micro-machining processes employs masks to specify the shape of the product. Two-dimensional shapes are the main outcome (Corbett et al., 2000).

A further characteristic of micro machining is the volume or size of the part removed from the workpiece. For example, in electrochemical machining the unit removal is defined as the size of atoms. Shape specification elements for process in which masks are used have to be considered. Since the mask specifies only two dimensions, these fabrication methods are usually applied to the production of thin or shallow shapes. Photo fabrication of this type has advanced considerably reducing pattern size in semiconductor devices, with dimensions below micrometer range already achieved and nanometric size are becoming attainable (Suda et al., 2000; Dantas et al., 2002; Wang, 2002). In most methods that rely on masks as shape specification elements, material removal is based on chemical or physical reactions on the atomic scale. Therefore, the unit of removal can be of the order of atomic quantities. The micro shaping of parts with geometrical features of dimensions 5 to 500 μm, with accuracy 1 to 10 μm, and the production of mirror-like surface finishes, have considerable industrial applications (Dario et al., 1995; Bhattacharyya and Munda, 2003). However, many well-established micro-fabrication technologies have some drawbacks such as limited geometry and narrow material selection. Hence, new avenues in micro-machining area are being attempted by exploiting the potential of other existing techniques (Rajurkar et al., 2006).

2. MICRO ELECTROCHEMICAL MACHINING (MICRO ECM)

In electrochemical machining (ECM) process, the material dissolution occurs when the workpiece is made as the anode in an electrolytic cell. A diagrammatic sketch of high precision micro ECM set-up is shown in Figure 1. The cathode tool is separated from the anode by a narrow electrolytic spacing (gap) through which electrolyte flows with high velocity. However, in micro ECM the inter-electrode gap control plays an important role. The resolution of machining shape is better for very small machining gap (Chikamori, 1998; DeSilva and McGeough, 1998). For the range of dimensional accuracies required in micro machining, lower inter-electrode gaps need to be in the order of 20 μm (Lee et al., 2002). The utilization of pulsed power in normal ECM has given it better process control over its dimensional tolerances. The application of ultrashort voltage pulses in electrochemical machining can improve the precision down to the lower nanometer range, fully retaining three-dimensional structuring capabilities (Kock et al., 2003; Bhattacharyya et al., 2004; Datta et al., 1996).

2.1. Micro ECM Techniques

2.1.1. Micro ECM through-Maskless

Thin-film patterning by maskless micro ECM requires high-localized material removal induced by the impingement of a fine electrolytic jet (Rajurkar et al., 1999; Kozak et al., 1996; El-Taweel, 2003). A micro electrochemical jet machining (micro EJM) was developed to obtain micro indent for oil film formation on rolling bearing (Datta et al., 1989). Micro EJM removes material by using an electrolyte jet from a small nozzle, which works as cathode without advancement of the jet as shown in Figure 2(a). High aspect ratio holes are drilled by using a fine cathode tool in the form of a capillary that is advanced at constant rate towards the workpiece as shown in Figure 2(b). Investigation of jet and laser-jet micro ECM demonstrated that neutral salt solution could be effectively used for high-speed micro machining of many alloys (Rajurkar et al., 1999).

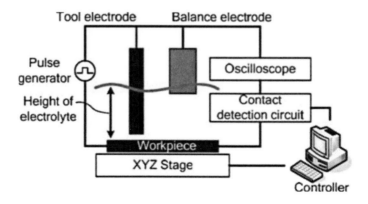

Figure 1. Diagrammatic sketch of micro ECM set-up.

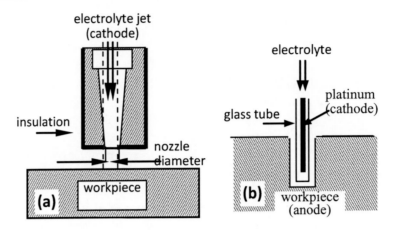

Figure 2. Different types of maskless micro ECM. a) Micro EJM b) Capillary drilling.

2.1.2. Micro ECM through-Mask

Micro ECM in conjunction with a photoresist mask is of considerable interest in microelectronic fabrication. Micro ECM through-mask involves selective metal dissolution from unprotected areas of a one- or two-sided photoresist-patterned workpiece. Through-mask metal removal by wet etching is accompanied by undercutting of the photoresist and is generally isotropic in nature. In isotropic etching, the material is removed both vertically and laterally at the same rate. This is particularly the case in chemical etching, where the etch boundary usually recedes at a 45° angle relative to the surface (Datta, 1998). In micro ECM, the metal-removal rate in the lateral direction may be significantly reduced through proper consideration of mass transport and current distribution (Rajurkar et al., 1999).

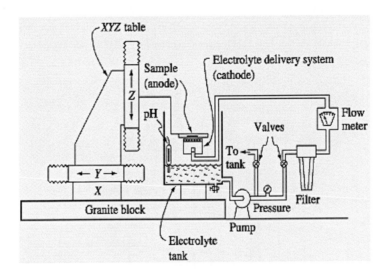

Figure 3. Experimental system for one-sided micro ECM (Datta, 1998).

Figure 3 shows experimental system for one-sided micro ECM of through-mask micro ECM. The tool consists of a driving XYZ table for sample movement and an electrolyte delivery system in the form of a multi-nozzle assembly, which acts as the cathode. The sample is held in a stationary sample holder while the multi-nozzle cathode, which is attached to the table, moves at a constant speed facing the sample. The inter-electrode spacing is kept constant at 1-3 mm. A 25 mm wide multi-nozzle flow assembly provides high speed electrolyte impingement at the dissolving surface thus permitting effective removal of the dissolved products and of the heat generated by joule heating. The tool can be used for micro ECM for samples of different sizes (Datta, 1998).

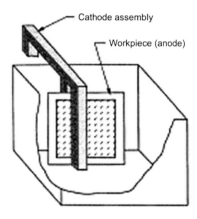

Figure 4. Schematic diagram of two-sided micro ECM (Datta, 1998).

Figure 4 shows schematic diagram of two-sided micro ECM tool that was recently developed for high-speed fabrication of molybdenum masks (Datta and Landolt, 2000). The tool uses a novel concept of localized dissolution induced by scanning two cathode assemblies over a vertically held workpiece providing movement of the electrolyte. Highly localized dissolution by using a small cathode width and an extremely small inter-electrode spacing provide directionality of metal removal and uniformity of current distribution. The electrolyte flows into the cathode assembly and then flows across the cathode surface between the cathode and the mask anode. Depending on the aspect ratio of features desired, two different flow types could be used in the tool, namely; a shearing flow from top to bottom (Figure 5(a)), and an impinging flow directed into the mask anode (Figure 5(b)) (Datta and Landolt, 2000; Datta and Harris, 1997; Landolt et al. 2003).

2.2. Micro ECM Applications

Micro ECM technology is expected to play an increasingly important role in the electronics and micro-systems industry because of its cost effectiveness and achievable high precision. In addition, electrochemical processes are attractive from an environmental point of view because material deposition or removal is highly selective thus minimizing waste (Masuzawa, 2000).

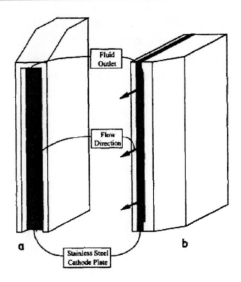

Figure 5. Two types of electrolyte delivery systems (Datta, 1998)a) Shearing flow; b) Impinging flow.

2.2.1. Fabrication of Microelectronic Components

Maskless and through-mask micro ECM as the fabrication of components such as print bands for high-speed printers, metal masks for screening and evaporation, inner planes for high-density circuitization. Moreover, these techniques are used in fabrication of copper lines for printed-circuit boards, slider suspension for magnetic recording, cone connectors for pad-on-pad connector contacts, and flip-chip interconnects (Datta and Romankiw, 1994; DeSilva et al., 2000).

2.2.2. Ink-jet Nozzle Plates

The fabrication of nozzle plates by micro ECM involves the following steps (Lloyd et al., 1988). The cleaned metallic foil is laminated with photoresist on both sides of the foil. The photoresist on one side is then exposed and developed to define the initial pattern, consisting of an array of circular openings. A controlled micro ECM process is employed to fabricate flat-bottomed, V-shaped nozzles on the sample. The photoresist is then stripped, and the sample is inspected for entry and exit holes. A 25 μm thick stainless steel foil was laminated with 25 μm thick photoresist on both sides (Figure 6). The photoresist on one side was exposed and developed for patterning, while the blanket photoresist on the backside of the foil served as a protective insulating layer.

Direct and pulsed-voltage experiments were performed using a neutral salt solution of sodium chloride and glycerol mixture as the electrolyte. The final nozzle shape was determined by several factors that included undercutting; etch factor, dissolution time, and dissolution conditions. Pulsating-voltage micro ECM was found to be effective in providing dimensional uniformity of nozzles. On a 25 μm thick stainless foil patterned with a 55 μm diameter photoresist opening, a targeted exit-hole dimension of 55 μm was achieved with a standard deviation below 2. A desired nozzle angle of 27° was produced (Abate et al., 1996; Bhattacharyya and Munda, 2003).

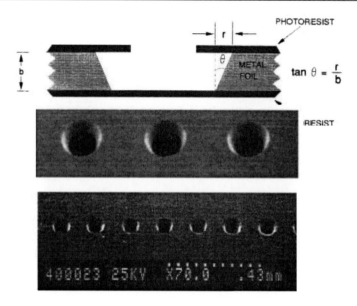

Figure 6. Ink-jet nozzle plate fabricated by through-mask micro ECM. Schematic of the concept (top) and a photograph showing an array of nozzles (bottom) (Lloyd et al.1988).

2.2.3. Metal Masks

In the microelectronics industry, etched metal masks are used for pattern definition in conductor screening and evaporation processes. Lead-frame production also requires patterned metal sheets that are either etched or stamped (Yong et al., 2003; Masuzawa et al., 1994). Large volumes of patterned metal sheets are used in the production of aperture masks for color CRTs. A variety of metal and alloy sheets are used, including iron, stainless steel, copper, brass, and nickel-iron alloys. For the most demanding applications in screening and evaporation processes in microelectronics, molybdenum is the material of choice (Lee et al., 2007).

Fabrication of metal masks involves through patterning by etching of a foil that is coated with perfectly aligned patterned photoresist on two sides. In a typical present day processing, molybdenum masks are etched in a spray etcher using heated alkaline potassium ferricyanide solution. The solution will lose its etching activity as a larger quantity of the ferricyanide is reduced to ferrocyanide. Larger-volume users regenerate the etchant electrochemically or by using a chemical oxidizer such as ozone. The spent etchant must be disposed of as a hazardous waste. In addition, the rinse water from the etching operation must also be segregated and treated as a hazardous waste stream. Two systems for treating the hazardous waste stream are crystallization and ion exchange (Datta and Harris, 1997).

2.2.4. Micro Hole Drilling

Micro-hole drilling seems to be a simple process, but requires adequate consideration about process control and machining techniques. Side-insulated electrode, micro gap control between the cathode and anode, and pulsed current are synthetically utilized (DeSilva and McGeough, 1998; Munda and Bhattacharyya, 2008). The side-insulation of electrode and micro gap control contribute directly to localized machining. The pulsed current put on the cathode and anode has a function to agitate electrolyte, so as to promote the electrochemical reaction (DeSilva and McGeough, 1998; Kock et al. 2003; Wang et al 2007). Figure 7(a) shows a micro hole electrochemically machined in 10% $NaClO_3$ solution under DC current. A side-insulated electrode with diameter of 302 μm is used. The electrode material is tungsten and a thin SiC insulating layer is coated on it via chemical vapor deposition (CVD). The machining gap is controlled in the range of 15-20 μm and the hole diameter about 420 μm is obtained on stainless steel plate with depth of 200 μm. In micro-machining gap, the electrolyte is easily boiled by the high concentration of the machining current. However, if pulse voltage used, these problems could be eliminated. The temperature of the electrolyte is cooled down and the dregs are swept off during the pulse-off duration (DeSilva and McGeough, 1998).

Figure 7(b) shows a micro hole electrochemically machined in 10% $NaClO_3$ solution by using a pulse voltage with pulse duration of 0.5 ms and an interval of 0.5 ms. A copper electrode with diameter of 180 μm is side-insulated with Lucite. Hole diameter about 220 μm is obtained on stainless steel plate with depth of 300 μm through machining gap control. With comparison to DC current, the enlarged part of hole diameter compared to the electrode is much reduced by means of pulse current. Further improvement of the machining precision could be possible with even shorter pulses (Figure 8) (Munda and Bhattacharyya, 2008; Park et al., 2006).

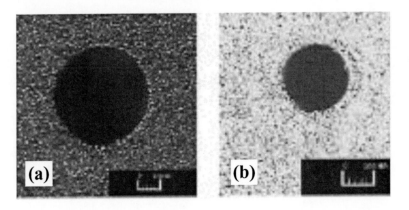

Figure 7. Photograph of micro holes produced by: a) DC current b) Pulse current (Chikamori, 1998).

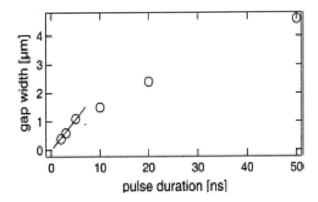

Figure 8. Gap width at different pulse duration.

2.2.5. Micro Surface Production

Micro ECM has been used to produce the micro structuring of surface such as micro grooving to a depth of several micrometers for self-acting fluid film bearings. To control microgrooves precisely and have homogeneous current distribution, a cathode with a non-conducting part has been developed. A pulse ECM process model to predict the machining depth has been also developed for the analysis of the inter-electrode gap mechanism (Munda and Bhattacharyya, 2008; Choi et al., 2007).

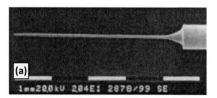

Figure 9. Fabrication examples of micropin (Park et al., 2006). a) Cylindrical micropin (dia.50 μm and length 4 mm). b) Stepped micropin used as micro-tool for micro EDM (dia. of the last part is 10 μm).

Figure 10. Schematic presentation of two approaches to fabrication of a two level structure using micro ECM through a photoresist a) Large cavity etched prior to small groove b) Grooves etched prior to large cavity.

Cylindrical micro-pins are widely used as a micro-tool for micro machining of 3D mechanical micro-parts and used as micro-tool for micro EDM (Figure 9). Recent researches indicate the suitability of EMM for surface finishing micro-pin and micro-spindles (Rahman et al., 2006; Hyung et al., 2001; Lim and Kim, 2001; Ferri et al., 2001; Sen and Shan, 2005). The overall pin profile fabricated using process is governed by two conflicting effects, the effect of geometry and the effect of diffusion layer. Accurate pin profiling is accomplished by controlling the current density and voltage, which determine the effect of diffusion layer (Park et al., 2006). Cylindrical micro-pins are widely used as a micro-tool for micro machining of 3D mechanical micro-parts and used as micro-tool for micro EDM (Figure 9). Recent researches indicate the suitability of micro ECM for surface finishing micro-pin and micro-spindles (Rahman et al., 2006; Hyung et al., 2001; Lim and Kim, 2001; Ferri et al., 2001; Sen and Shan, 2005). The overall pin profile fabricated using process is governed by two conflicting effects, the effect of geometry and the effect of diffusion layer. Accurate pin profiling is accomplished by controlling the current density and voltage, which determine the effect of diffusion layer (Park et al., 2006).

More recently, the application of micro ECM to the fabrication of two level structures has been explored. Two approaches were compared in Figure 10: (a) etching of the large cavity followed by application of a resist and etching of the grooves, (b) etching of the grooves, followed by fabrication of the large cavity in a second step. Both approaches involve two applications of photoresist and two dissolution steps (Lohrengel et al., 2003).

3. MICRO ELECTRODISCHARGE MACHINING (MICRO EDM)

3.1. Micro EDM Techniques

Electrical Discharge Machining (EDM) is a non-conventional machining technique in which the material is removed by the erosive action of electrical discharges (sparks) provided by a generator. The discharges result from an electrical voltage that is applied between the two electrodes: the tool and the workpiece. The dielectric fluid separates these electrodes. Every discharge (or spark) melts a small amount of material on both electrodes. The net result is that each discharge leaves a small crater on both workpiece and tool electrode.

The same phenomenon of EDM is applied at the micron level for micro machining. The process is called as micro electrodischarge machining (micro EDM). True micro EDM processes only commenced when Kurafuji and Masuzawa (1967) succeeded in machining 6 μm diameter circular holes through cemented carbide 50 μm thick, thus demonstrating the rapid production of high aspect ratio holes. Since that time, there has been a concern effort to improve the rate of micro machining of various materials, without loss of accuracy and improve the high quality of surface finish and dimensional control already associated with the technique of EDM (Masuzawa, 1985).

In EDM, the amount of material removed is a function of the energy, which crosses the discharge gap. In micro EDM, small energy is the key point to make micro products with high accuracy and good surface finish, the energy per single discharge should be minimized and discharge frequency should be increased (Zhang et al., 2000). It is required for micro machining to maintain the energy of a single discharge in the order of 10^{-6}J to 10^{-7}J. A configuration of micro EDM apparatus is shown in Figure 11.

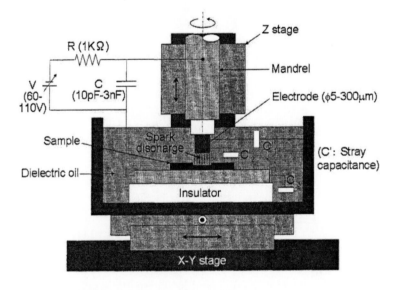

Figure 11. Configuration of micro EDM apparatus.

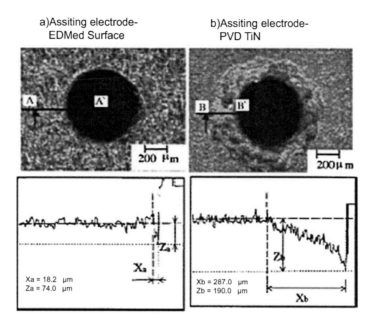

Figure 12. Comparison of cross-sectional shape between micro EDM on the TiN coating and the EDMed surface (Mohri et al., 2003).

3.2. Micro EDM Applications

3.2.1. Micro EDM of Ceramics

Nowadays, advanced ceramics, such as silicon nitride (Si_3N_4), boron carbide (B_4C) and silicon-infiltrated silicon carbide (SiSiC), are found in many fields of application. Many three-dimensional complex shapes have been machined out of insulating ceramics such as Si_3N_4, ZrO_2, and SiC by EDM (Fleischer and Kotschenreuther, 2007; Nakaoku et al., 2007; Sa'nchez et al., 2001; Mohri et al., 2002). In this process, the EDMed surface is covered with the electrical conductive layer during discharge.

Muttamara et al. (2003) succeeded to machine Si_3N_4, ceramics by EDM. The technology is named as an assisting electrode method. This ability of micro EDM makes it play a very crucial role in the manufacture of micro mechatronic systems. The layer holds the electrical conductivity during discharge. For micro EDM, the wear of tool electrode becomes lager than the normal machining. So, the micro machining is extremely difficult to get precision sample (Fukuzawa et al., 1998).

When the assisting electrode layer has the same value of electrical conductive layer, the discharge is generated continuously with the same machining conditions from the assisting electrode to ceramics. In this case, the entrance area of hole machining kept a fine precision shape as shown in Figure 12 (a). On the TiN assisting electrode, a thermally affected zone was detected around the entrance area of the hole. The width of thermally affected zone attained to about half of the tool electrode diameter of 200 μm. It is impossible to get the narrow machining distance among other machined holes alternatively (Mohri et al., 2003). As shown in Figure 12(b), the fine entrance shape machining can be accomplished. Wuthrich et al. (1999) presented 3D high aspect ratio structuring of glass by combining ECM with EDM called ECDM technology. The process can be described as follows. The glass sample is dipped in an electrolyte solution together with two electrodes. Applying constant voltage between these electrodes, sparks are generated which erodes the glass. Figure 13 shows the complex structure, which has been generated by this technology.

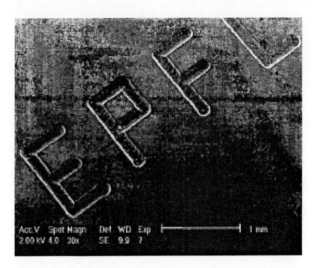

Figure 13. Complex channel machined on Si_3N_4 by micro ECDM (Mohri et al., 2003).

3.2.2. Micro Electrodes for EDM and Micro-Pins

Wire electrodischage grinding (WEDG) was suggested for ultra-micro structure fabrication technologies. In WEDG method by micronizing the material removal unit from ultra-minimizing the energy level per unit discharge pulse, it is possible to improve the degree of machining accuracy. The principle of WEDG is illustrated in Figure 14. The tool electrode is a metal wire, which slides slowly along a groove in a wire guide. The wire movement prevents the tool wear problem associated with the process.

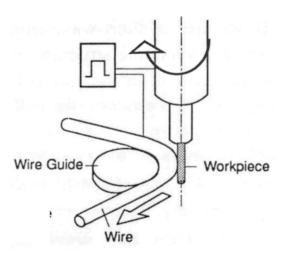

Figure 14. Principle of WEDG.

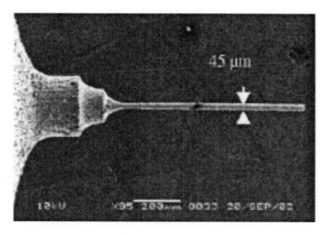

Figure 15. Example of 45 μm CuW electrode (Masuzawa et al., 1985).

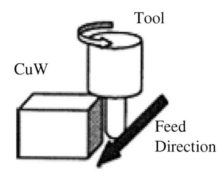

Figure 16. Example of microelectrode made by rectangular CuW block.

Typically a WEDM machine is used to make cylindrical electrodes with diameters down to 5μm electrodes are to be used for micro EDM die-sinking of precision holes. These microelectrodes need to be straight and have a high length-to-diameter (L/D) ratio so that many holes can be fabricated before it wears away. The L/D ratio obtained depends on the electrode material and the required electrode diameter. Copper–tungsten material is usually used on the micro EDM as a tool electrode because of its rigidity and low wear. Masuzawa et al. (1985) have successfully produced micro-electrodes and micro-pins using micro EDM and a combined electrical machining process. Figure 15 shows an example of 45 μm CuW electrode fabricated by WEDG. Electrodes having a square cross-section (50x50 μm) are now being used to fabricate sharp-cornered cavities and slots width greater than the electrode width. Normal ED sinking is also a possible method that can be used to machine micro-pins and micro-spindles (Ali and Ong, 2006; Mohri and Tani, 2006) as shown in Figure 16. A rectangular block is used as the electrode instead of wire and wire guide in WEDG. This type of application is often called reverse EDM, or sometimes (micro EDG).

3.2.3. Ink-Jet Nozzle

Micro EDM is applied to minute curved surfaces to form super fine nozzles like those used for fuel injection in diesel engines and to make the high precision metal masking for printing used in the electronic device manufacturing processes. High aspect ratio machining can be done using the process. Moreover, the micro EDM produces very small burrs, much smaller than those seen in mechanical drilling and milling operations and therefore does not need subsequent deburring operations.

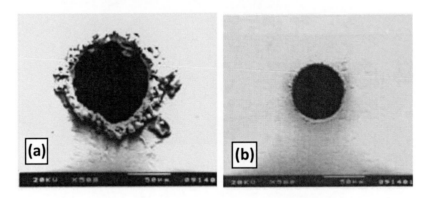

Figure 17. SEM photographs of micro hole on copper plate (diameter of electrode is 50 μm) (Guitrau, 1997). Positive polarity b) Negative polarity.

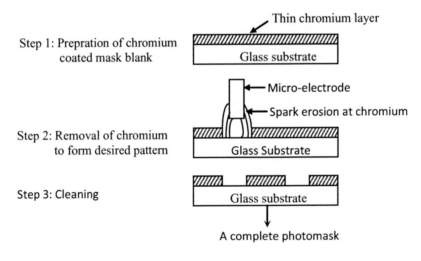

Figure 18. Proposed micro EDM technique by Yeo and Yap, 2001.

In continuous ink jet printing, a jet of ink is emitted from a nozzle under pressure and broken into a stream of uniform droplets by the application of ultrasonic vibration. A manufacturing process that can produce reliable, densely packed and precise ink jet nozzles was introduced in Japan in 1986 (Sato et al., 1986), which uses micro EDM. The level of energy used to drill holes is very small, being about one hundredth of a micro joule. Ink jet orifices were machined into thin foils made of different grades of stainless steel by micro EDM (Allen and Lecheheb, 1996). The results of study founded that the quality of the nozzles produced by micro EDM increases as the energy input decreases.

3.2.4. Micro Hole Drilling

Recently, the need for metallic products containing micro holes has been shown a pronounced and steady growth. For micro-hole generation with diameters smaller than 0.1 mm, when compared with the usual utilization of the electro-erosion process, the most important parameter to be monitored and evaluated is the erosion speed. The erosion speed is a function of a series of factors, such as: current intensity; physical characteristics of the material to be machined, pulse duration (T_{on}), polarity and pause duration (T_{off}). Figure 17 shows SEM photographs of a micro hole in the copper plate. The hole expansion and electrode wear for negative polarity machining seems to be larger (Guitrau, 1997; Kaminski and Capuano, 2003). To improve the productivity of micro parts using the micro EDM process, a batch production method of micro-holes by micro EDM using multi-electrodes has been developed by Weng and Her (2002). Reynaerts et al. (1997) developed a micro EDM machining method capable of drilling a hole with a diameter of 160 μm and depth of 380 μm within 2 min. A machining method that compounds micro EDM and micro ultrasonic vibration lapping (MUVL) for producing micro-holes with a diameter about 100 μm was also proposed (Wang et al., 2002; Sundaram et al., 2008; Wang et al., 2005; Murali and Yeo, 2004).

3.2.5. Micro Surface Production

The micro EDM process was conducted as an alternative technique for producing photo masks for use in micro-electromechanical system (MEMS). Yeo and Yap (2001) examined the effects and characteristics of machining thin conductive films coated on a non-conductive substrate (borosilicate glass) using micro EDM. Figure 18 shows the steps of the proposed micro EDM technique for producing photo masks.

4. MICRO LASER MACHINING (MICRO LM)

Laser systems are being increasingly employed in many diverse micro-systems technology (MST) sectors such as biomedicine, automotive manufacture, display devices, telecommunications, printing technologies and semiconductors. These applications areas are using lasers in different ways ranging from basic research and development stages to full production environments (Crafer and Oakley, 1993; Chen and Darling, 2005; Jha et al., 2007; AbdelMalek, 2003; Bednarczyk et al., 1999).

In micro laser machining technology, material removal takes place actually through the ablation process. The surface area under laser irradiation absorbs the beam energy and is transformed into either a liquid or a vapor. When the temperature of the irradiated surface reaches the boiling point of the material, the absorbed radiation energy causes the vaporization of the material and dissipates to the areas at lower temperature. Hence, the entire energy released from the laser beam will be spent in both heating and providing the latent heat of vaporization. When the incident laser beam intensity is larger than $1 \times 10^{10} \sim 5 \times 10^{10}$ W/cm^2, the laser beam energy forms a plasma at the surface area and the vaporization phenomenon is dominant, rather than the melting phenomenon, during the interaction of the laser beam with materials (Ready, 1997). Two laser systems which are at the forefront of industrial integration, and whose applications have reached a high level of production maturity, are excimer lasers (mask projection techniques) and Nd: YAG lasers (Direct writing techniques).

4.1. Micro LM Techniques

4.1.1. Mask Projection Technique

The majority of excimer laser systems used in manufacturing applications use the technique of mask projection (Harvey and Rumsby, 1997). This method is particularly suited to excimer lasers since their optical properties mean that direct beam focussing is not usually an attractive option and projection methods can be utilized more efficiently in the production of various microstructures. Mask projection methods used with excimer lasers can provide many desirable features. In standard mask projection systems, the depth of the micro-structures is controlled by the numbers of laser shots which are fired and the resolution of the features are determined by the mask and the optical projection system (Rizvi, 1999). Standard mask projection techniques are very versatile and depth information can be imparted into micro machined samples by an appropriate synchronization of the sample position and the laser firing sequence (Rizvi et al., 1997). The level of control of the depth profile required in the above-mentioned applications, however, means that these standard methods are not extended far enough. To overcome this limitation, a new technique, synchronised overlay scanning (SOS), has been developed (Figure 19) (Rizvi and Apte, 2002).

4.1.2. Direct Writing Technique

In direct write systems, the laser beam is focused to a small spot using a lens and either the beam or the sample (or both) is moved around to produce the desired pattern (Figure 20). Beam spot sizes of a few tens of microns can be easily achieved with such systems and the combination of scanner mirrors and high repetition rate lasers means that very high processing speeds can be achieved. Hence, the process can be termed step-and-scan since the processing is performed for a scan field, the laser turned off, the sample moved to the position of the next scan field and the patterning re-started. This stepping aspect of this process, when no processing is taking place, obviously causes an increase in the total patterning time. Even though the stepping time delay is only a few hundreds of milliseconds, it can produce significant cumulative effects on total processing times for large samples, which in turn can severely impact the economic attractiveness of the whole process (Harvey and Rumsby, 1997).

4.2. Micro LM Applications

4.2.1. Micro Machining of Electrostatic Electron Lenses

Miniaturized electron beam micro columns with an overall length of a few mm from an emitter to the last electrode (electron lens) of the enisled lens attract considerable attention. This is due to their greatly reduced size and weight which is expected to lead to various kinds of new applications in semiconductor equipments, such as a miniaturized Scanning Electron Microscope (SEM), inspection and metrology systems, electrical testing systems, and eventually productive electron beam lithography (Dubey and Yadava, 2008; Cheng et al.,

2006). Micro LM technology would be a promising candidate technology in fabricating micron size apertures on a thin membrane. The electrostatic electron lens in a miniaturized electron beam system consists of several circular apertures fabricated in a Si membrane.

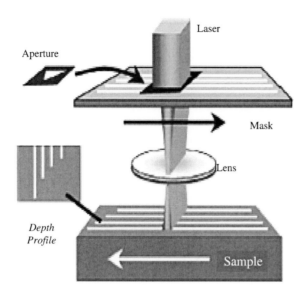

Figure 19. Technique of SOS.

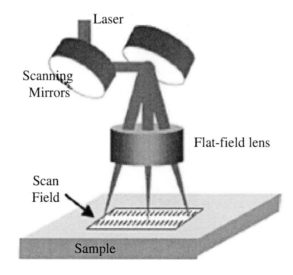

Figure 20. Technique of direct writing.

For a miniaturized electron beam system application, miniaturized electrostatic electron lenses and their assembly, called a micro column, have been fabricated using an active Q-switched 1.06 µm Nd: YAG pulsed laser beam having a pulse width of 10 ns. The laser micro machining condition for 20 µm thick Si membrane has been investigated by Ahn et al. (2003). Figure 21 represents the experimental setup for the laser micro machining of an aperture at the center of the Si membrane. Active Q-switched Nd: YAG laser beam was focused onto the specimen through a beam expander and a focusing lens.

4.2.2. Micro Hole Drilling

A pulsed Nd: YAG laser is a typical of many industrial uses for drilling and cutting. Guo et al. (2003) presented a new laser drilling method based on the gelcasting technology. The irregular spatter at the exit of the hole and micro cracks produced by the traditional laser drilling method can be effectively prevented by direct laser drilling of gelcast green body and compact micro holes with much more regular shapes without micro cracks can be successfully obtained. As can be seen in Figure 22, the holes drilled by two pulses on sintered ceramics are encircled with large area of irregular spatter deposits.

Jackson and Neill (2003) determined laser micro drilling etch rate and surface structure. The interaction phenomena of nanosecond time period, Q-switched, diode pumped Nd: YAG laser pulses using 1064, 532 and 355 nm wavelengths with M2 tool steel was investigated at an incident laser intensity range between 2 and 450 GW/cm^2. The authors (Guo et al., 2003; Jackson and Neill, 2003; Dhara et al., 2008) reported that the decrease in the drilling etch rate as the interaction wavelength is increased, is thought to occur due to the reflective nature of tool steel and absorption of laser radiation by the plasma formed above the material during high intensity laser–material interaction.

4.2.3. Manufacturing of 3D Structures

During last years, especially in the electronic production areas, an increasing tendency for miniaturization of the structure size has been observed. This is known as micro system technique. A high precision laser machine for 3D structuring has been developed (Ihlemann et al., 2000; Molpeceres et al. 2007; Crawford et al. 2005; Heyl et al. 2001). Laser processing of hard metals and ceramics with ultra-violet (UV) light (355 nm) was studied and optimised with respect to surface quality (Heyl et al., 2001). It could be shown that the surface smoothness of the structures produced by laser ablation in metals is equal to that produced by high quality electrodischarge milling. This laser ablation technology is ideally used for production of ceramic injection nozzles (Pfleging et al., 2002). Other fields of applications are dielectric masks, injection moulds, moulds for galvanoforming, 2D, 3D laser marking and structuring. Some geometries example in WC/Co (tungsten carbide sinterd in a cobalt matrix) have been viewed with a Scanning Electron Microscope (SEM) and are shown in Figure 23 (Heyl et al., 2001; Pfleging et al., 2002; Snakenborg et al., 2004).

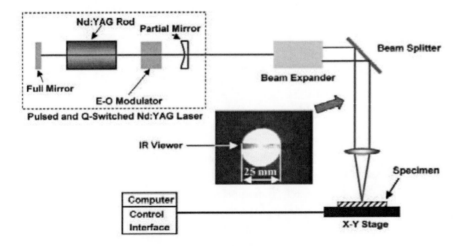

Figure 21. Experimental set-up of the micro LM for Si membrane.

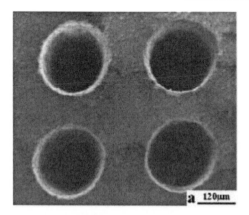

Figure 22. SEM micrographs of the holes drilled on gelcast green body (Guo et al., 2003).

Figure 23. SEM photograph of example geometries in WC/Co: The structures were ablated with a 5μm
X–Y-grid. Ablation depth was approximately 1.3 μm per layer resulting in a total ablation depth of 130
μm (Heyl et al. 2001).

5. MICRO ULTRASONIC MACHINING (MICRO USM)

The emergence of micro-electromechanical system (MEMS) has strongly enhanced the use of newer and harder work materials, namely; brittle materials, and their micro-machining technologies. Ultrasonic machining (USM) is the use of tool ultrasonically vibrated. When combined with favorable abrasive slurry, USM creates desired accurate cavities of any shape through the impact grinding of fine grains. Ultrasonic machining process is non-thermal, non-chemical and thus can produce a high-quality surface finish. However, as tool machining technology, conventional USM is not capable, for instance, of drilling micro-holes smaller than 100 μm for lack of corresponding co-axial micro-tools (Thoe et al., 1998; Sun et al., 1996; McGeough, 2002). Micro ultrasonic machining (micro USM) is such a technology that enables breakthroughs in making almost any three-dimensional microstructure with high aspect ratio in most materials, particularly brittle materials, such as silicon, borosilicate glass, silicon nitride, quartz and ceramics. Micro USM may also be a good way of obtaining superior surface finish for micro-parts.

5.1. Micro USM Tools

The essentials of the micro USM system are given in Figure 24, where mainly WEDM, EDM and USM and their related controlling and positioning unit are shown. The micro USM is mainly divided into two stages as shown in Figure 25. The WEDG/EDM combination is used to generate co-axial micro-tool first, which micro USM of brittle materials carried out. To this end a combined machine exploiting wire electro-discharge grinding (WEDG), EDM and USM functions itself has been developed. The co-axial micro-tools are prepared by the WEDG/EDM combination first, and then applied directly in ultrasonic machining without any tool chucking problem. A micro USM comprises of a vibrated tool, a slurry supply unit and the machine body, which makes motion and provides a table for mounting the workpiece (Thoe et al., 1998). Irregular shaped hard abrasive particles are dispersed in a liquid medium (abrasive slurry) and fed into the gap between tool and workpiece. The tool is vibrating with an ultrasonic frequency (usually 20~40 kHz) with an amplitude of several to tens micrometers. When static load is applied between tool and workpiece, abrasive particles impact and chip away material from both workpiece and to a lesser extent from the tool (Sun et al., 1996). Condition of the abrasive and its grain size affect the machining rate (Thoe et al., 1998). A continuous flow of abrasive slurry flushes away the debris from the working zone. Since actual machining is carried out by abrasive particles, the tool can be softer than the workpiece.

Tool wear is the major intrinsic drawback of USM. Especially in micro machining with micro-tools, the longitudinal and lateral (side or diametral) tool wear become more serious and some extent determine the micro machining accuracy. Sun et al. (1996) reported that the most popular tool material in conventional USM, such as thoriated tungsten and stainless steel, are no longer suitable for micro machining due to their large wear.

5.2. Micro USM Applications

5.2.1. Micro Hole Drilling

All materials tending to a brittle fracture behavior can be machined by micro USM. Examples include high performance ceramics, glass, graphite and a part of the fiber-reinforced plastics (Ghahramani and Wang, 2001; Medis and Henderson, 2005; Yu et al., 2005). For drilling micro-holes with high aspect ratios in borosilicate glass, a working method combining micro EDM with micro USM was developed by Yan et al. (2002). Highly accurate micro-holes with diameters of about 150 μm and depth of 500 μm were manufactured in borosilicate glass via the micro USM method. A circular micro-tool was produced using the micro EDM process. This tool was then used to drill a hole in glass using the micro USM process. Micro USM process produced square hole and inclined hole with aspect ratios all over five.

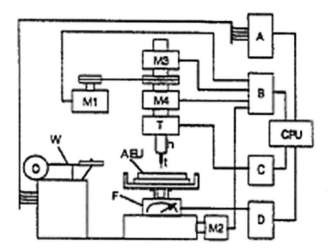

Figure 24. Micro USM machine: A, processing circuits for WEDG; B, driving and positioning unit; C, electronic oscillation generator; D, electronic weight display; M1, M2, M3, M4, motors; T, transducer; W, WEDG unit; F, force sensor.

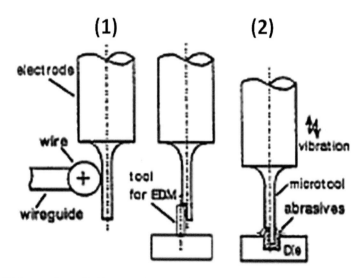

Figure 25. Micro USM procedure. 1)Micro-tool preparation; 2) Structure machining.

The using of appropriate machining parameters; the diameter variations between the entrances and exits (DVEE) could reach a value of about 2 µm in micro-holes with diameters of about 150 µm and depths of 500 µm. Furthermore, DVEE improves if an appropriate slurry concentration; ultrasonic amplitude or rotational speed utilized. The machining tool rotation speed has a close relationship to the degree of micro-hole roundness. Micro-holes with a roundness error value of about 2 µm could be obtained if the appropriate rotational speed was employed. Figure 26 presents micro-holes with acceptable entrances and exits produced at 150 rpm rotational speed (Yan et al., 2002).

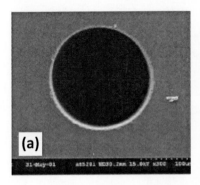 

Figure 26. The shapes of micro-holes at rotational speed of 150 rpm through micro USM (Yan et al., 2002). a) The entrance of the micro-hole. b) The exit of the micro-hole.

Figure 27. SEM photograph of the micro air turbine. Center pin diameter 70 µm; rotor diameter 350 µm (Sun et al., 1996).

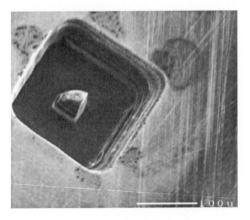

Figure 28. SEM photograph 3D cavity machined by micro USM (Moronuki et al., 2004).

5.2.2. Manufacturing of 3D Structures

There are two techniques of achieving microstructure on brittle materials. One of these techniques is by directly duplicating the convex micro-tool shape into the concave structures and the other is by writing microstructures with simple tool by controlling their multi-axis movements. Generally for simple concave structure, for instance, micro-hole boring, only direct duplications were needed, whereas for complex 3D microstructure making, multi-axis movements were often required. As an application combining micro-hole boring and trench writing by multi-axis movement, a micro-turbine chamber was fabricated (Zhang et al., 2005).

Micro USM is a combined machining method with a strong capability of dealing with various 3D microstructures of almost any material. So, the self-aligned multi-layer machine and assembly of 3D complex micro-machines become possible on the same machine. In order to demonstrate these techniques, a micro center-pin bearing air turbine was introduced and fabricated. Figure 27 shows a SEM photograph of the micro air turbine (Sun et al., 1996). The overall dimensions are 850 µm height and 950 µm diameter. The rotor and its bearing are 350 µm and 70 µm in diameter, respectively.

Slotting on low melting glass has been reported in (Yan et al., 2002). The tool wear compensation strategy "Uniform Wear Method" originally developed for micro EDM has been applied in micro USM to successfully generate 3D micro cavities as shown in Figure 28 (Moronuki et al., 2004).

7. SUMMARY AND CONCLUSIONS

Technological advances made in micro machining using non-conventional machining processes, which reflect the state of the art in academic and industrial achievements and applications, have been presented in this paper. It is clear that non-conventional processes have emerged as an indispensable part of micro-manufacturing technologies. A comparison of non-conventional micro machining processes is given in Table 1.

Table 1. Comparison of non-conventional micro machining processes (Sen and Shan, 2005; Rajurkar et al. 2006; Masuzawa, 2000; McGeough, 2002)

Characteristic	Micro ECM	Micro EDM	Micro LM	Micro USM
Cutting rate (mm/s)	0.125	0.0125	<1	0.425
Work material	Electrically conductive	Electrically conductive	Any materials	Harder than 40 HRC (Brittle materials)
Surface integrity	No residual stress, no burr	Heat affected surface, no burr	Presence of HAZ, taper	Gentle
Operating voltage	1-15	30–100	4.5 kV	220
Geometric complexity	Good	Good	Fair	Good
Mass production	Poor	Poor	Poor	Poor
Surface quality	Fair	Fair	Fair	Fair

Electrochemical metal removal in micro fabrication, which include both through-mask and maskless, offers many advantages including the possibility of patterning a variety of conducting materials at high speed, using electrolyte that pose minimized safety and waste disposal problems. Another key advantage is the possibility of controlling the surface finish during metal removal. An essential criterion for the development of an effective micro ECM process is to employ precision tool that provides high rate of uniform mass transport at the dissolving workpiece surface.

Since micro EDM provides such advantages as the ability to manufacture complicated shapes with high accuracy, and process any conductive materials regardless of hardness, it has become one of the most important methods for manufacturing micro-parts. Wire electro-discharge grinding is the most promising method so far, to produce micro-pin and micro-spindle.

Two laser systems, which are at the forefront of industrial integration, and their applications have reached a high level of production maturity, are excimer lasers and Nd: YAG lasers. Excimer laser ablation is a versatile tool for the micro machining of various materials.

Micro USM is a machining method with a strong capability of dealing with various 3D microstructures of almost any material with high aspect ratio, particularly brittle materials. Metal etching techniques are widely employed in the fabrication of microelectronic package, metallic components and micro-engineered structures.

The applications presented in this paper demonstrate the opportunities offered by non-conventional micro-machining processes not only on the micro-electronic scale but also in other industries such as the aerospace and medical fields. Products made using these technologies include spinning nozzles, blanking dies, gears, optical parts, blanking punches, drawing dies, coining dies, fluidic devices, molds for optical devices, texturing tools, medical parts and medical tools.

REFERENCES

Abate, K., Datta, M. and McDougall, B.R and Fenton, J.M. (1996) 'High rate metal dissolution processes', Ed. PV 95-19, *The Electrochemical Society,* p.157.

AbdelMalek, F. (2003) 'Study of a Micro-machined tunable all air gap vertical cavity surface emitting laser', *Materials Letters,* Vol. 57, p.2198.

Ahn, S., Kim, D., Kim, H., Ahn, S.J. and Cho, J. (2003) 'Fabrication of a miniaturized electron lens system and laser micro-machining condition for silicon membrane', *Microelectronic Engineering,* Vol., 69, p.57.

Allen, D.M. and Lecheheb, A. (1996) 'Micro electro-discharge machining of ink jet nozzles: optimum selection of material and machining parameters', *J. Mater. Process. Technol.,* Vol., 58, p.53.

Ali, M.Y. and Ong, A.S. (2006) 'Fabricating micro milling tool using wire electrodischarge grinding and focused ion beam sputtering' *Int J Adv Manuf Technol,* Vol. 31(5/6), p.501.

Bednarczyk, S., Bechir, R. and Baclet, P. (1999) 'Laser micro-machining of small objects for high-energy laser experiments', *Appl. Phys.,* Vol. A 69, p.495.

Bhattacharyya, B., Doloi, B. and Sridhar, P. (2001) 'Electrochemical micro-machining: new possibilities for micro-machining', *J. Mater. Process. Technol.,* Vol. 113, p.301.

Bhattacharyya, B. and Munda, J. (2003) 'Experimental investigation on the influence of electrochemical machining parameters on machining rate and accuracy in micro-machining domain', *Int. J. Machine Tools Manufac.* Vol., 43, p.1301.

Bhattacharyya, B. and Munda, J. (2003) 'Experimental investigation into electrochemical micromachining (EMM) process', *J. Mater. Process. Technol.* Vol., 140, p.287.

Bhattacharyya, B., Munda, J. and Malapati, M. (2004) 'Advancement in electrochemical micro-machining', *Int. J. Machine Tools Manufac.* Vol. 44, p.1577.

Cheng, Y., Tsai, H.L., Sugioka, K. and Midorikawa, K. (2006) 'Fabrication of 3D microoptical lenses in photosensitive glass using femtosecond laser micro machining', *Applied Physics A: Materials Science & Processing,* Vol. 85(1), p.11.

Chen, T. and Darling B. (2005) 'Parametric studies on pulsed near ultraviolet frequency tripled Nd:YAG laser micromachining of sapphire and silicon', *J. Mater. Process. Technol.,* Vol. (169), p.214.

Choi, S.H., Ryu, S.H., Choi, D.K. and Chu, C.N. (2007), 'Fabrication of WC micro-shaft by using electrochemical etching', *Int J Adv Manuf Technol,* Vol., 31(7/8), p.682.

Chikamori, K. (1998) 'Possibilities of electrochemical micro-machining' *Int. Japan Soc. Precision Engineering,* Vol. 32, p.37.

Corbett, J., McKeown, P.A., Peggs, G.N. and Whatmore, R. (2000) 'Nano-technology: international development and emerging products', *Annals of the CIRP,* Vol. 49(2), p.524.

Crawford, T.R., Borowiec, A. and Haugen, H.K. (2005) 'Femtosecond laser micro machining of grooves in silicon with 800 nm pulses', *Applied Physics A: Materials Science & Processing,* Vol. 80(8), p.1717.

Crafer, R.C. and Oakley, P.J. (1993) *'Laser processing in manufacturing',* Chapman & Hall, London.

Datta, M., Masuko, N., Osaka, T. and Ito, Y. (1996) *'Electrochemical micro machining in electrochemical technology: innovations and new developments'* Eds. Kodansha/Gordon and Breach, Tokyo, p.137.

DeSilva, A. and McGeough, J.A. (1998) 'Process monitoring of electrochemical micro-machining', *J. Mater. Process. Technol.,* Vol. 76, p.165.

DeSilva, A., Atlena, H.J. and McGeough, J.A. (2000) 'Precision ECM by process modeling', *Annals of the CIRP,* Vol. 49 (1), p.151.

D'Arrigoa, G., Coffab, S. and Spinellaa, C. (2002) 'Advanced micro-machining processes for micro-opto-Electromechanical components and devices', *Sensors and Actuators,* A99, p.112.

Dantas, O.S., Galeazzo, E., Peres, E.M. and Femandz, R. (2002) 'Silicon micro mechanical structure fabricated by electrochemical process', *IEEE*7803-7454, p.575.

Dario, P., Carozza, M., Croce, M., Montesi, M.C. and Cocco, M. (1995) 'Non-traditional technologies for micro-fabrication', *Journal of Micromech. Microeng.* Vol. 1, p.64.

Datta, M., Romankiw, L.T., Vigliotti, D.R. and Gutfeld, R.J. (1989) 'Jet and laser-jet electrochemical micro-machining of nickel and steel', *J. Electrochemical Soc.* Vol. 136, p.2251.

Datta, M. (1998) 'Micro fabrication by electrochemical metal removal', *IBM Journal of Research and Development,* Vol. 42/5, p.655.

Datta, M. and Landolt, D. (2000) 'Fundamental aspects and applications of electrochemical microfabrication', *Electrochimica Acta,* Vol. 45, p.2535.

Datta, M. and Harris, D. (1997) 'Electrochemical micro machining: an environmentally friendly, high speed processing technology', *Electrochimica Acta,* Vol. 42, p.3007.

Datta, M. and Romankiw, L.T. (1994) 'In electrochemical technology applications in electronics', Eds. PV 93-20, *The Electrochemical Society,* 123; US Patent 5,284,554.

Dhara, S.K., Kuar, A.S. and Mitra, S. (2008) 'An artificial neural network approach on parametric optimization of laser micro-machining of die-steel', *Int J Adv Manuf Technol.,* Vol. 39 (1/2), p.39

Dubey, A.K. and Yadava, V. (2008) 'Experimental study of Nd:YAG laser beam machining-an overview', *J. Mater. Process. Technol.,* Vol. 195 (1/3), p.15.

Dubey, A.K. and Yadava, V. (2008) 'Laser beam machining - *A review International Journal of Machine Tools and Manufacture,* Vol. 48 (6), p. 609.

El-Taweel, T.A. (2003) Electrochemical jet finishing (ECJF) of cylindrical components', *Proceedings of the 20th International Manufacturing Conf.* (IMC-20), Cork, Ireland Sept. 3-5: p.509.

Ferri, Y., Pietrowski, O., Chauvy, P.F., Madore, C. and Landolt, D. (2001) 'Recent advance in the study of electro-chemical micro-machining', *J. Micro-mechanical Micro-engineering, Vol.11, p.522.*

Fleischer, J. and Kotschenreuther, J. (2007) 'The manufacturing of micro molds by conventional and energy-assisted processes' *Int J Adv Manuf Technol,* Vol. 33(1/2), p.75.

Fukuzawa, Y., Katougi, H., Mohri, N., Furutani, K. and Tani, T. (1998) 'Machining properties of ceramics with an electric discharge machine', *Proceedings of the ISEM* XII, p.445.

Ghahramani, B. and Wang, Z.Y. (2001) 'Precision ultrasonic machining process: a case study of stress analysis of ceramic (Al_2O_3)', *Int. J. Machine Tools Manufac.,* Vol.. 41(8), p.1189.

Guitrau, E.B. (1997) 'The EDM handbook', Hanser Gardner Publications, Cincinnati.

Guo, D., Cai, K., Yang, J. and Huang, Y. (2003) 'Spatter-free laser drilling of alumina ceramics based on gel-casting technology', *Journal of the European Ceramic Society,* Vol. 23, p.1263.

Harvey, E.C. and Rumsby, P.T. (1997) 'Fabrication techniques and their application to produce novel micromachined structures and devices using excimer laser projection' *Proceedings of the SPIE Conference on Micro machining and Micro fabrication Process Technology* III, Vol. 3223, p.26.

Heyl, P., Olschewski, T. and Wijnaendts, R.W. (2001) 'Manufacturing of 3D structures for micro-tools using laser ablation', *Microelectronic Engineering,* 57/58, p.775.

Hyung, J.L., Young, M.L., Soo, H.K. and Yoon, K.K. (2001) 'Electrochemical fabrication method for micro punch', *7th Int.Conf. on Prod. Engg. Design and Control,* Egypt, p1097.

Ihlemann, J. and Rubahn, K. (2000) 'Excimer laser micro-machining: fabrication and applications of dielectric mask', *Applied Surface Science,* 154/155, p.587.

Jackson, M.J. and O'Neill, W. (2003) Laser micro-drilling of tool steel using Nd: YAG lasers', *J. Mater. Process. Technol.,* Vol. 142, p.517.

Jha, H., Kikuchi, T., Sakairi, M. and Takahashi, H. (2007) 'Laser micro machining of porous anodic alumina film', *Applied Physics A: Materials Science & Processing,* Vol. 88(4), p.617.

Kaminski, P. and Capuano, M. (2003) 'Micro hole machining by conventional penetration electrical discharge machine', *Int. J. Machine Tools Manufac.,* Vol. 43, p.1143.

Kozak, J., Rajurkar, K.P. and Balkrishna, R. (1996) 'Study of electrochemical jet machining Process', Trans. of ASME, *J. of Manufact. Science and Engineering,* Vol.118, p.990.

Kock, M., Kirchner, V. and Schuster, R. (2003) 'Electrochemical micro machining with ultrashort voltage pulses a versatile method with lithographical precision', *Electrochimica Acta,* Vol. 48, p.3213.

Kurita, T., Chikamori, K., Kubota, S. and Hattori, M. (2006) 'A study of three-dimensional shape machining with an ECμM system', *Int. J. Machine Tools Manufac.,* Vol. 46(12/13), p.1311.

Kuafuji, H. and Masuzawa, T. (1967) 'EDM of Micro-holes in Cemented Carbide Alloys', *Proc. of Annual Autumn Assembly of JSPE,* p.77.

Landolt, D., Chauvy, P.F. and Zinger, O. (2003) 'Electrochemical micro machining, polishing and surface structuring of metals: fundamental aspects and new developments', *Electrochimica Acta,* Vol., 48, p.3185.

Lee, E.S., Park, J.W. and Moon, Y.H. (2002) 'A study on electrochemical micro machining for fabrication of microgrooves in an air-lubricated hydrodynamic bearing', *Int. J. Adv. Manuf. Tech.,* Vol. 20, p.720.

Lee, E.S., Baek, S.Y. and Cho, C.R. (2007) 'A study of the characteristics for electrochemical micromachining with ultrashort voltage pulses', *Int J Adv Manuf Technol,* Vol., 31 (7/8), p.762.

Lim, Y.M. and Kim, S.H. (2001) 'An electrochemical fabrication method for extremely thin cylindrical micropin', *Int. J. Machine Tools Manufac.,* Vol. 41, p.2287.

Lloyd, W.J., Taub, H.H., Durbeck, R.C. and Sherr, S. (1988) *'In output hard copy devices',* Eds. Academic Press, Inc., New York.

Lohrengel, M., Kluppel. I., Rosenkranz, C., Bettermann, H. and Schultze, J. (2003) 'Microscopic investigations of electrochemical machining of Fe in NaNO$_3$', *Electrochimica Acta,* Vol. 48, p.3203.

Masuzawa, T., Fujino, M. and Kobayashi, K. (1985) 'Wire electrodischarge grinding for micro-machining' *Annals the CIRP,* 34(1), p.431.

Masuzawa, T., Fujino, M., Kobayashi, K. and Suzuki, T. (1985) 'Wire electrodischarge grinding for micro-machining', *Annals of the CIRP,* 34 (1), p.431.

Masuzawa, T., Yamamoto, M. and Fujino, M. (1989) 'A micro punching system using wire-EDM', *Proceedings of the International Symposium for Electromachining* (ISEM-9), p.86.

Masuzawa, T., Kuo, C. and Fujin, M.A. (1994) 'Combined electrical machining process for micro-nozzle fabrication' *Annals the CIRP,* 43(1), p.189.

Masuzawa, T. and Tanshoff, H.K. (1997) 'Three dimensional micro-machining by machine tools', *Annals of the CIRP,* 46(2), p.621.

Masuzawa, T. (2000) 'State of the art of micro-machining', *Annals of the CIRP,* 49 (2), p.473.

Masuzawa, T., Kuto, C.L. and Fujino, M. (1994) 'A combined electrical machining process for micro-nozzle fabrication', *Annals of the CIRP,* 43 (1), p.189.

Masuzawa, T. (1985) 'An approach to micromachining through machine tool technology', *Annals of the CIRP,* 34 (1), p.419.

McGeough, J.A. (2002) *'Micro machining of engineering materials',* Marcel Dekker Inc., New York.

Medis, P.S. and Henderson, H.T. (2005) 'Micro machining using ultrasonic impact grinding', *Journal of Micromechanics and Microengineering,* Vol.15(8), p.1556.

Mohri, N. and Tani, T. (2006) 'Micro-pin electrodes formation by micro-scanning EDM process', *CIRP Annals,* 55(1), p.175.

Mohri, N., Fukuzawa, Y. and Tani, T. (2002) 'Some considerations to machining characteristics of insulating ceramics towards practical use in industry', *Annals of the CIRP,* 51(2), p.112.

Mohri, N., Fukusima, Y., Fukuzawa, Y., Tani, T. and Saito, N. (2003) 'Layer generation process on workpiece in electrical discharge machining', *Annals of the CIRP,* 53(1), p.81.

Moronuki, M., Saito, Y., Kaneko, A., Miura, A. and Aikawa, C. (2004) 'Vibration micromachining of low-melting-temperature glass', *7th International Symposium on Advances in Abrasive Technology,* Bursa, Turkey, p.489.

Molpeceres, C., Lauzurica, S., García-Ballesteros, J.J., Morales, M. and Ocaña, J.L. (2007) 'Advanced 3D micro machining techniques using UV laser sources', *Microelectronic Engineering,* Vol. 84(5/8), p.1337.

Munda, J. and Bhattacharyya, B. (2008) 'Investigation into electrochemical micromachining (EMM) through response surface methodology based approach', *Int J Adv Manuf Technol.* Vol. 35 (7/8), p.821.

Murali, M. and Yeo, S.H. (2004) 'A novel spark erosion technique for the fabrication of high aspect ratio micro-grooves', *Microsystem Technologies,* Vol. 10(8/9), p.628.

Muttamara, A., Fukuzawa, Y., Mohri, N. and Tani, T. (2003) 'Probability of precision micro-machining of insulating Si_3N_4 ceramics by EDM', *J. Mater. Process. Technol.,* Vol. 140, p.243.

Nakaoku, H., Masuzawa, T. and Fujino, M. (2007) 'Micro-EDM of sintered diamond', *J. Mater. Process. Technol.,* Vol. 187/188, p.274.

Park, B.J., Kim, B.H. and Chu, C.N. (2006) 'The effects of tool electrode size on characteristics of micro electrochemical machining', *CIRP Annals,* 55(1), p.197.

Pecholt, B., Vendan, M., Dong, Y. and Molian, P. (2008) 'Ultrafast laser micro machining of 3C-SiC thin films for MEMS device fabrication', *Int J Adv Manuf Technol.,* Vol. 39 (3/4), p.239

Pfleging, W., Bernauer, W., Hanemann, T. and Torge, M. (2002) 'Rapid fabrication of micro-components-UV-laser assisted prototyping, laser micro-machining of mold inserts and replication via photomolding', *Microsystem Technologies,* 9, p.67.

Rahman, M.A., Rahman, M., Kumar, A.S., Lim, H.S. and Asad, .A.B (2006) 'Development of micropin fabrication process using tool based micro machining', *Int J Adv Manuf Technol,* Vol. 27(9/10), p.939.

Rajurkar, K.P., Zhu, D, McGeough, J.A., Kozak, J. and DeSilva, A. (1999) A New developments in electrochemical machining', *Annals of the CIRP,* 48(2), p.567.

Rajurkar, K.P., Levy, G., Malshe, A., Sundaram, M.M., McGeough, J., Hu, X., Resnick, R. and DeSilva, A. (2006) 'Micro and nano machining by electro-physical and chemical processes', *Annals of the CIRP,* 55(2), p.643.

Ready, J.F. (1997) *'Industrial Application of Lasers',* Academic Press, New York.

Reynaerts, D., Heeren, P.H. and Brussel, H.V. (1997) 'Micro structuring of silicon by elelctro-discharge machining (EDM)', Part I: *theory, Sensors and Actuators*, A60, p.212.

Rizvi, N.H. (1999) 'Production of novel 3D microstructures using excimer laser mask projection techniques', *Proceedings of the SPIE Conference on Design, Test and Micro fabrication of MEMS and MOEMS,* Vol. 3680, p.546.

Rizvi, N.H., Harvey, E.C., Rumsby, P.T., Burt, J.H., Talary, M.S., Tame, J.A. and Pethig, R. (1997) 'An excimer laser micro machining system for the production of bioparticle electro-manipulation devices', *Proceedings of the SPIE Conference on Micro machining and Micro fabrication Process Technology* III, Vol. 3224, p.266.

Rizvi, N.H. and Apte, P. (2002) 'Developments in laser micro-machining techniques', *J. Mater. Process. Technol.,* Vol. 127, p.206.

Sa´nchez, J.A., Cabanes, I., Lo´pez, L.N. and Lamikiz, (2001) 'A Development of optimum electrodischarge machining technology for advanced Ceramics', *Int. J. Adv. Manuf. Technology,* Vol. 18, p.897.

Sato, T., Mizutani, T., Yonemochi, K. and Kawata, K. (1986) 'The development of an electrodischarge machine for micro-hole boring', *Precision Eng.* 8(3), p.163.

Sen, M. and Shan, H.S. (2005) 'A review of electrochemical macro- to micro-hole drilling processes', *Int. J. Machine Tools Manufac.,* Vol. 45, p.137.

Snakenborg, D., Klank, H. and Kutter, J. (2004) 'Microstructure fabrication with a CO_2 laser system', *J. Micromech. Microeng.,* Vol. 14, p.182.

Suda, M., Furata. K., Sakuhara, T. and Akata, T. (2000) 'The micro factory system using electrochemical machining', *Galvanotechnik,* Vol. 90, p.2607.

Sundaram, M.M., Pavalarajan, G.B. and Rajurkar, K.P. (i2008) 'A study on process parameters of ultrasonic assisted micro EDM based on Taguchi method', *Journal of Materials Engineering and Performance,* Vol. 17(2), p.210.

Sun, X-Q, Masuzawa, T. and Fujino, M. (1996) 'Micro ultrasonic machining and self-aligned multilayer machining/assembly technologies for 3D micro-machines', *Proc. IEEE Workshop on Micro Electro Mechanical System, Saan Diego,* CA., US, p.312.

Sun, X-Q, Masuzawa, T. and Fujino, M. (1996) 'Micro ultrasonic machining and its applications in MEMS', *Sensors and Actuators,* A57, p.159.

Thoe, T.B., Aspinwall, D.K. and Wise, M. (1998) 'Review on ultrasonic machining', *Int. J. Machine Tools Manufac.,* Vol. 38, No. 4, p.239.

Wang, J. (2002) 'Electrochemical detection for micro-scale analytical systems: a review', *Talanta,* Vol. 56, p.223.

Wang, A., Yan, B., Li, X. and Huang, F. (2002) 'Use of micro ultrasonic vibration lapping to enhance the precision of microholes drilled by micro electrodischarge machining', *Int. J. Machine Tools Manufac.,* Vol. 42, p.915.

Wang, A.C., Yan. B.H., Tang, Y.X. and Huang, F.Y. (2005) 'The feasibility study on a fabricated micro slit die using micro EDM', Int J Adv Manuf Technol, Vol. 25(1/2), p.10.

Wang, J., Chung, C.K., Wu, B.H. and Liao, Y.Y. (2007) 'Fabrication of wedge-shape tool via electrochemical micro machining with diamond-like carbon coating', *J. Mater. Process. Technol.,* Vol.187-188, p.264.

Weng, F, and Her, M. (2002) 'Study of the batch production of micro parts using the EDM process', *Int. J. Adv. Manuf. Technol.,* Vol. 19, p.266.

Wuthrich, R., Fascio, V., Viquerat, D. and Langen, H. (1999) 'In situ measurement and micromachining of glass', Int. Symposium on Micro mechatronics and Human Science, *IEEE,* p.185.

Yan, B.H., Wang, A.C., Huang, C.Y. and Huang, F.Y. (2002) 'Study of precision micro-holes in borosilicate glass using micro EDM combined with micro ultrasonic vibration machining', *Int. J. Machine Tools Manufac.,* Vol. 42, p.1105.

Yeo, S. and Yap, G. (2001) 'A feasibility study on the micro electro-discharge machining process for photomask fabrication', *Int. J. Adv. Manuf. Technol.,* Vol.18, p.7.

Yong, L., Yunfei, Z., Guanga, Y. and Liangqiang, P., (2003) 'Localized electrochemical micro machining with gap control', *Sensors and Actuators,* A108, p.144.

Yu, Z., Hu, X. and Rajurkar, K.P. (2005) 'Study of micro ultrasonic machining of silicon', *Proceedings of ASME International Mechanical Engineering Congress and Exposition,* Orlando, Florida US: 1-8.

Yu, Z.Y., Rajurkar, K.P. and Tandon, A. (2004) 'Study of 3D Micro-Ultrasonic Machining', *Journal of Manufacturing Science and Engineering,* 126(4), p.727.

Zhang, C., Rentsch, R. and Brinksmeier, E. (2005) 'Advances in microstructures in hard-brittle materials: A brief review and outlook', *Int. J. Machine Tools Manufac.,* Vol. 45(7/8), p. 881.

Zhang, Z., Zhu, D., Qu, N. and Wang, M. (2007) 'Theoretical and experimental investigation on electrochemical micro machining', *Micro-system Technologies,* Vol. 13 (7), p.607.

Zhang, C., Onmori, H. and Li, W. (2000) 'Precision shaping of small diameter wheels using micro-electricdischarge truing (MEDT) and hole machining of Al_2O_3 material', *Int. J. Machine Tools Manufac.,* Vol. 40, p.661.

In: Micro and Nanomanufacturing Research   ISBN 978-1-61942-003-8
Editor: J. Paulo Davim   © 2012 Nova Science Publishers, Inc.

Chapter 8

MANUFACTURING AND APPLICATION OF MICRO/NANO FLUIDIC DEVICES

Chong Liu*, Zheng Xu, Jun-sheng Liang,
Jing-min Li, Jun-shan Liu, Da-zhi Wang

Dalian University of Technology, Key Laboratory for Micro/Nano Technology and
System of Liaoning Province, Dalian, Liaoning Province 116085, China

ABSTRACT

Micro/nano fluidic technologies have experienced a rapid development over the past few years. Micro/nano fluidic devices present uniquely attractive opportunities and benefits for various applications in molecular and cellular biological analysis, microelectronics cooling, micropower, microreaction. Many micro/nano fluidic devices have been exploited and used to sample, trap, separate, sort and analyze biological materials. This chapter describes manufacturing and application of micro/nano fluidic devices. We emphasize a cross-disciplinary view and more technical details aren't included, but available in the listed references. In the first section, the basic components including nanochannel, micromixer, micropump and microvalve are described. Some critical criteria of the mechanisms for the adaptation of a given application are discussed. Then, a brief introduction to some typical materials and related manufacturing principles for the fabrication of micro/nano fluidic devices is given. An overview of the fabrication techniques for thermoplastics-based lab-on-a-chip devices as an example of Micro/Nano fluidic devices are provided in section 3. In section 4, some issues about micro direct methanol fuel cell (μDMFC) are discussed, including a simple description of historical background, silicon micromachining for μDMFC, micro photochemical etching of the stainless steel polar plates, and experiments of μDMFC performance testing.

---

* Corresponding author, E-mail: chongl@dlut.edu.cn

1. MICRO/NANO FLUIDIC COMPONENTS

Micro/nano fluidic devices offer uniquely attractive benefits for biological handling and analysis. Recently many complex micro/nano fluidic devices have been exploited and used to sample, trap, separate, sort and analyze biological materials. For a micro/nano fluidic device, the composed fluidic components are very important, which are connected to each other through microchannels. There are a number of considerations in selecting and designing components for a specific micro/nano fluidic device.

In this section, the basic components including nanochannel, micromixer, micropump and microvalve are described. Some critical criteria of the mechanisms for the adaptation of a given application are discussed.

1.1. NANOCHANNELS

The applications of nanofluidics are very promising in biotechnology and medicine. The nanometer length scale will allow the discovery of a new range of phenomena, where the feature size of the channel is on the order of atoms or molecules. Recently the reports about nanochannel-based devices increased significantly. But as the development of nanofluidics and related devices is still multi-directional and fast, it is very difficult to provide a complete list. This section just gives some typical examples.

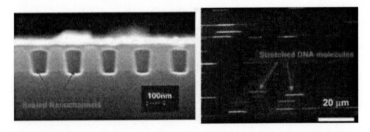

Figure 1.1. DNA stretching in nanochannel [1].Reproduced with permission from ACS.

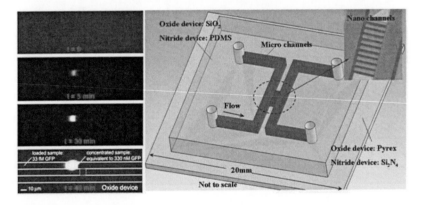

Figure 1.2. Preconcentration of GFP in the nanofluidic device [2]. Reproduced with permission from ACS.

1) *Figure* A major application of nanochannels is in the analysis of DNA. The special dimensions of DNA molecules are close to the cross-sectional size of nanochannel. That allows for a whole new way of detecting, analyzing and separating these bimolecular. Typically a DNA molecule will form a compact arrangement in its natural state. However, as shown in Figure 1.1, when a DNA molecule flows into a nanochannel, it will be more possible to keep a stretched state that simplifies the followed sequencing process greatly [1]. The phenomenon of DNA stretching is mostly attractive to some biological applications such as mapping of DNA segments.

2) *Figure* For the detection in trace amounts, the high S/N detection becomes increasingly difficult when the analyze concentration is lower than the detection limit. To overcome the drawback, Han et al [2] demonstrated a nanochannel-based electrokinetic trapping mechanism that can achieve more than a million fold preconcentration, as shown in Figure 1.2. The key of electrokinetic trapping preconcentration is a set of nanochannels that are small enough to produce electrical double layer overlapping and these nanochannels work as ion selective membranes that can generate concentration polarization or space charge extension with the use of the applied field strength.

3) *Figure* Molecular filtration and sieving is an important engineering problem, with wide applications, such as c bio-analytic separation and water purification. Han et al have successfully constructed a nanofilter array chip that can fractionate protein complexes and DNA molecules in several minutes. Nanofilter arrays with a gap size of 40-180nm were fabricated. The nanofilter array chip can be used without degradation.

4) *Figure* Nanochannels have been used to create a nanofluidic transistor based on a metal oxidesolution system [3], as shown in Figure 1.3. It was demonstrated that gate voltages are able to modulate the concentration of ions and molecules in the channel and control ion conductance. This is because the height of the nanochannel is on the order of or smaller than the Debye length for the ionic solutions. Therefore, the electric field from the gate can precisely control ion flow.

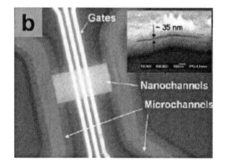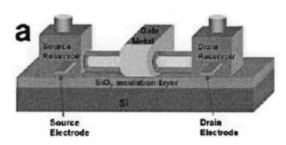

Figure 1.3. Nanofluidic transistor devices [3]. Reproduced with permission from ACS.

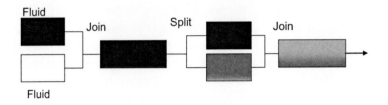

Figure 1.4. The principle of serial lamination mixing and a serial micromixer.

1.2. Micromixers

Rapid Sample mixing is essential in the microfluidic systems for biochemistry analysis, drug delivery and chemical reactions. However, the typical microfluidic environment exhibits laminar flow, in which the diffusion is the main mixing mechanism. A real challenge is to develop driven mixer that can be used to enhance the diffusion rate. Different principles for enhancing fluid mixing have been reported. Micromixers can be mainly categorized as active micromixers and passive micromixers.

Passive micromixers do not require external energy, and the mixing process entirely relies on diffusion or chaotic advection. So the main idea for the optimization of the mixing behavior in passive micromixers is to increase the contact surface of different type fluids and to induce chaotic advection. In general, the passive mixers can be subdivided into four categories:

1) *Serial lamination micromixers.* In a serial lamination micromixer (Figure 1.4) the fluids are repeatedly spited and recombined in microchannel to exponentially increase their interfacial area [4].

2) *Parallel lamination micromixers.* A parallel lamination micromixer splits the inlet streams into a number of substreams, and then joins them into one stream as laminae. As shown in Figure 1.5, the basic design is a long microchannel with two inlets connected to its geometry. The designs are often T-type mixer [5] or Y-type mixer [6].

Figure 1.5. Parallel lamination micromixers: T-type mixer and Y- type mixer.

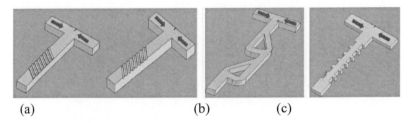

(a)   (b)   (c)

Figure 1.6. Chaotic advection micromixers.

3) *Chaotic advection micromixers.* Chaotic advection micromixers often mean using 3D geometries in microchannel or complex microchannels, for example twisted one or serpentine one, to generate chaotic advection and consequently rapid mixing can be achieved [7]. Many microstructures have been used for produce chaotic advection, including rips or grooves on the channel for mixing (suitable for Re<10) (Figure 1.6.a), C-shaped segments or Tesla structures (suitable for 10<Re<100) (Figure 1.6.b), entire insert obstacles structures (suitable for Re>100 (Figure 1.6.c).

4) *Injection mixer. Instead* of splitting both inlet flows, this mixer only splits the solute flow into many streams and injects them into the solvent flow. On top of one stream is an array of nozzles, which create a number of microplumes of the solute. As a result, the interface area increases and mixing efficiency is improved.

On the contrary, an active micromixer need external power. The external energy induces the various disturbances to enhance the diffusion and the convection for mixing. For example, pressure field disturbance can be used to enhance mixing with a T-type mixer. The disturbance strength is controlled *via* the driving force from inlets. Another method of pressure field disturbance is the generation of pulsing velocity, which makes fluids exchange energy to each other significantly. Other methods of disturbance for active mixers include pneumatic disturbance, electroosmotic disturbance, magneto hydrodynamic disturbance, and thermal disturbance.

Generally, active mixers have better performance than passive ones in the term of the mixing efficiency. These mixers can be activated and adjusted to make the devices reconfigurable and controllable. However, the requirement of external power makes them difficult to integrate with other microfluidic devices. The fabrication process is usually complicated. Compare with the passive micromixers, passive micromixers are simple to operate because the mixing process occurs along with the structure change of microchannel, making them attractive and suitable for integration.

In order to quantify the percentage of mixing, the concentration profiles at the cross section of downstream are normalized using the followed equation. The equation quantifies the amount of mixing based on the standard deviation of the concentration profile from that of the perfectly mixed case [8].

$$\text{Percentage   mixed} = \left(1 - \frac{\sqrt{\dfrac{1}{N}\sum_{i=1}^{N}(c_i - \bar{c})^2}}{\sqrt{\dfrac{1}{N}\sum_{i=1}^{N}(c_i^o - \bar{c})^2}} \right) \times 100\%$$

where N , c_i, c_i^o, and $\bar{c}$ are the total number of points examined in the cross-stream direction, the concentration at each point, the concentration at each point if no mixing were to have taken place, and the concentration of the perfectly mixed case, respectively. The variable $\bar{c}$ can also be described as the mean concentration of the bulk fluid. At any location, values of c_i^o (the concentration at each point if no mixing were to have taken place) switch between

$c^*=0$ and $c^*=1$ as injections flow past. In practice, it is not necessary to explicitly calculate c_i° because both injections of $c^*=0$ and $c^*=1$ result in a constant denominator value of 0.5 in the equation.

1.3. Micropumps

Micropumping technology plays a core role in micro/nano fluidic applications and is utilized in various compact systems. A wide variety of technologies have been developed for micropumping. Micropumps can be classified into two categories: mechanical displacement micropumps, electro hydrodynamic (EHD) and magneto hydrodynamic(MHD) micropumps.

Mechanical displacement micropumps are defined as those that exert pressure forces on the working fluid through boundaries. Then the EHD and MHD micropumps are defined as those that provide a direct force to pump fluids *via* the additional energy from electric-field or magnetic field.

Mechanical displacement micropumps mainly include diaphragm pumps, peristaltic pumps, and phase-change pumps. The technology of diaphragm micropumps is the most widely studied and used in all micropumps.

As shown in Figure 1.7, diaphragm micropumps are usually comprised of a pumping chamber which is connected to inlet valve and outlet valve, one diaphragm on the side of the pumping chamber [9]. The reciprocation of this diaphragm actuated by external forces can produce the pumping action. The pumping process can be divided into the expansion stroke and the compression stroke. Due to the diaphragm deflects during the expansion stroke, the pumping chamber expands and the pressure in chamber decreases. As the inlet pressure is higher than the chamber pressure, the liquid will fill in the expanding chamber from inlet. During the compression stroke, the volume of the chamber decreases with the moving diaphragm, causing the internal pressure to increase whereby liquid is discharged through the outlet valve. Diaphragm displacement profiles are generally symmetric resulting in non-directional flow. Hence, in order to convert the non-directional flow into directional flow, valves are necessary.

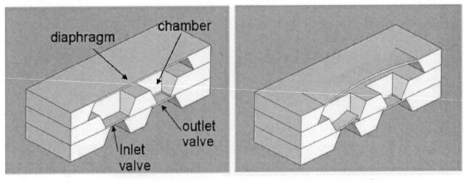

(a) Undeflected position.   (b) Expansion stroke.

Figure 1.7.(Continued).

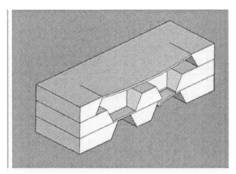

(c) Compression stroke

Figure 1.7. Diaphragm micropump (cutaway view).

The diaphragm can be driven through piezoelectric effect, electrostatic effect, electromagnetic and so on. For example, in a diaphragm pump driven via piezoelectric effect, the piezoelectric material is bonded to or deposited on the diaphragm for actuation and the applied AC voltage drives the expansion and compression strokes as the signal changes in polarity.

Most of the peristaltic pumps employ pneumatic driving. Pneumatic pumps exploit fluctuations through gas pressure on a diaphragm to effect vibration. As gas pressure is applied on the diaphragm, deflection occurs for the compression stroke. Then as the gas pressure takes out, the diaphragm resumes in the expansion stroke. As shown in Figure 1.8, incorporating the pneumatic motion of actuators in series will generate peristaltic pumping action. Due to the simple fabrication process, capable of being integrated and low material cost, the pneumatic peristaltic pumping is mostly attractive. The micropumps consisting of three PDMS membranes are often designed and used. When one micropump is activated, the other two served as microvalves simultaneously [9]. Comparing to the diaphragm micropump, its main advantage is the capability of providing bidirectional flows.

Phase change micropumps utilize volume changes from phase transition such as liquid-to-vapor [10], to displace fluid for pumping.

EHD and MHD micropumps directly convert electrical and magnetic forms of energy into fluid motion. Since these pumping processes occur in a continuous manner, the resulting flow is generally constant and steady. Moreover EHD and MHD can gain their directionality from the applied field without valves.

EHD pumps utilize electrostatic forces on ions, and then drag the bulk fluid flow due to fluid viscosity. There are mainly two types of EHD pumps: induction-type EHD pump and ion-drag EHD pump. Induction-type EHD pumps require a gradient in the electrical conductivity or permittivity of the fluid. This can be achieved by anisotropic fluid heating or by discontinuities in other properties. The ion-drag EHD pumping uses the interaction of an electric field with electric charges, dipoles or particles in fluid to move the fluid. The electric field is established between a charged electrode and a grounded electrode. The Coulomb force that is produced by an external electrical field acts on all charges in the fluid. As a result the ions in liquid will move and drag the working fluid through the friction.

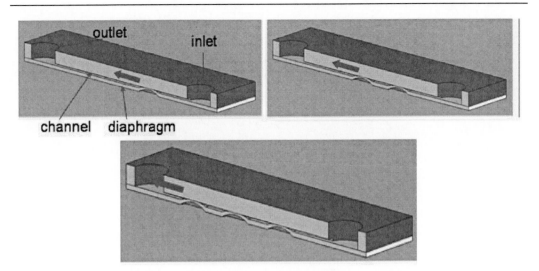

Figure 1.8. The principle of peristaltic micropump (cutaway view).

For a MHD micropump, a transversal ionic current inside the microchannel is subjected to a magnetic field oriented in an angle of 90° to current direction and microchannel axis. The Lorentz force acting onto the ionic current in the aqueous solution will then induce a fluid flow in the microchannel direction.

1.4. Microvalves

Generally microvalves are integrated with diaphragm micropumps to provide the flow rectification (section1.3). Similar to the micromixer, microvalves can be categorized as active microvalves, using mechanical and non-mechanical moving parts as well as external systems, and passive microvalves, using mechanical and non-mechanical moving parts.

1) *Active mechanical microvalves.* Various actuation principles are adopted to actuate mechanical moving parts in active microvalves. Most active microvalves couple a flexible diaphragm to magnetic, electric, shape memory alloy or other methods. For example, thermopneumatic microvalves are performed by volumetric thermal expansion coupled to diaphragm deflection. Typically, as shown in Figure 1.9, it has an actuator, a sealed chamber, and a movable diaphragm [11]. The medium in the chamber is heated by the heater and expand. As a result, the diaphragm will deflect to close the flow.

2) *Active non-mechanical microvalves.* Typically, the active non-mechanical microvalves are based on phase change mechanism. The active non-mechanical microvalve includes hydrogel microvalves, paraffin microvalves and ice microvalves. For example, ice microvalve is also called Peltier-actuated microvalve, since Peltier device is used to cool or heat the medium and it is relatively easy to reach −10 C from room temperature. Typically, for an ice microvalve, a microchannel is adjacent to a small thermoelectric Peltier cooler that is used to freeze

the partial liquid to block channel. The ice valve can be reopened by reversing electric current to turn it into a heater.

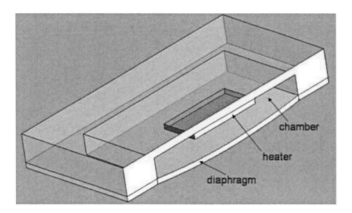

Figure 1.9. Thermopneumatic microvalve.

3) *Active external microvalves.* They include modular built-in valves, thin membrane and in-line microvalves actuated by external pneumatic air pressure or vacuum. Among them, pneumatic valves are actuated in a similar manner of pneumatic peristaltic pumps for flow rectification. Diaphragm valves are closed and opened using a proper pressure and a vacuum respectively, and they are used in conjunction with fluid barriers to position and manipulate reagents.

4) *Passive mechanical microvalves.* Most passive mechanical microvalves are placed in inlets and outlets of reciprocal displacement micropumps, such as flaps, membranes and spherical balls. Similar to the diode, passive valves only open to forward pressure. The principle of the cantilever-type flap microvalves with micropump is shown in Figure 1.7.

5) *Passive non-mechanical microvalves.* The Passive non-mechanical microvalves can be subdivided into fixed geometry valves and capillaryforce-based valves. Fixed geometry valves, including nozzle-diffuser valves and Tesla valves, employ no moving parts or boundaries for flow rectification. Rather, the geometry is fixed and the conversion of non-directional flow into directional flow occurs through geometries. The nozzle-diffuser valves (Figure 1.10.a) are based on the direction-dependent behavior of tapered microchannel [12]. For a tapered microchannel with an angle less than 20, the flow has lower flow resistance along the diffuser direction and larger flow resistance along the convergent nozzle flow direction.Tesla valves (Figure 1.10.b) are bifurcated channels in which the separated flow re-enters the main flow channel perpendicularly when the flow is in the reverse direction [9].

Capillaryforce-based valves are mainly based on electrocapillary, thermocapillary or passive capillary. These effects depend on various localized difference of surface characteristic on the channel surface[13].

The simplicity of their design and the low risk of clogging are the main advantages of fixed geometry valves. But the efficiency of fixed geometry valves is relatively poor, since these valves are always simi-open. Relatively, active diaphragm valves can overcome such shortcomings and withstand large-back pressure. However, the use of the active valves has the risk of fatigue and the fabrication process is more complicated too.

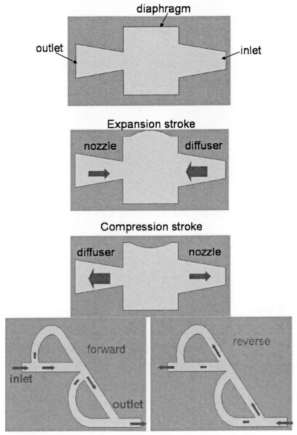

Figure 1.10. Fixed geometry valves.

2. MATERIAL AND MANUFACTURING TECHNIQUES

In this section, we will discuss some typical materials and related manufacturing principles for the fabrication of micro/nano fluidic devices.

2.1. Silicon and Glass

For some micro/nano fluidic devices, silicon and glass are still the preferred materials. The advantage of silicon and glass include mechanical rigidity, chemical resistance and low permeability properties, especially the glass have the property of optical transparency. The well developed micromachining technique provides the capability to obtain microstructures with high precision and repeatability using silicon and glass. In addition, the fabrication of scaling device dimensions down to the nanometer scale is relatively straight forward using silicon and glass micromachining.

Silicon (Si) is the major material in micromachining as it has excellent material properties, including a tensile strength, Young's modulus comparable to steel, a low density and thermal coefficient of expansion. Si micromachining is developed from integrated circuit fabrication technology. It has been remarkably extended in the past two decades. Surface micromachining, bulk micromachining, substrate bonding and electroforming et al can be used for Si micromachining. As the reports about Si micromachining are greatly abundant, this section will not cover the in-depth discussion about the Si micromachining. As the Si is opaque, it is frequently combined with glass or polymers to construct multiplex micro/nano fluidic devices.

Several types of glass have been used for micro/nano fluidic devices, including Pyrex, quartz, and borosilicates. The wet chemical etching with HF-based solutions is generally effective. But as the characteristic of glass wet etching is isotropic, the cross section of etched channel is always arc-like. In order to make anisotropic microstructures, dry etching techniques, such as plasma reactive ion etching, are required.

To complete the fabrication of a micro/nano fluidic device, it is necessary to seal two or more plates together. For a Si-glass-based chip, anodic bonding is effective to connect silicon plate to glass plate. For a full glass-based chip, high-temperatures bonding processes are often employed.

2.2. Polydimethylsiloxane

Polydimethylsiloxane (PDMS), an elastomeric silicone rubber, is often used for micro/nano fluidic applications. It has many advantages to other materials used in microfluidic assays such as glass or silicon. PDMS as a material is inexpensive, flexible, and optically transparent down to 230 nm. It is compatible with biological studies because it is impermeable to water, nontoxic to cells, and permeable to gases. The PDMS plate can be bonded to various substrates, including PDMS, glass, silicon and even other polymers.

A special PDMS kit, the Sylgard 184 from Dow Corning, is mostly widely employed for micro/nano fluidic devices. It has a two-part heat curable system that is often mixed in a 1:10 ratio of curing agent and PDMS monomers. The PDMS micro/nano fluidic devices are mostly fabricated with soft lithography. Briefly the scheme of PDMS soft lithography process is described as follows:

1) Fabrication of master. The master for soft lithography is necessary. The materials of template can be silicon, glass, metal and so on. An economic and simple method is to make epoxy structures on a Si wafer via common lithography. The surface silanization process of master is recommended in order to avoid adhering.
2) Mixing PDMS. Mix the curing agent and monomers in a 1:10 ratio.
3) Degassing. After the mixing, the silicone mixture will be full of air bubbles and the degassing process *via* vacuum is required.
4) Dispensing. Dispense the silicone without bubbles on to the template.
5) Spreading. Pick up the template with a pair of flat tweezers and start tilting it at a low angle. The material will now start to spread.
6) Curing and Pealing off. The PDMS is cured at 70°C for one hour or more and peeled off the master, producing the final replica bearing the designed microstructures.

2.3. Thermoplastic Polymer

Thermoplastic polymers are a class of synthetic polymers which exhibit softening behavior above a characteristic glass transition temperature (T_g) resulting from long-range motion of the polymer backbone, while returning to their original chemical state upon cooling. Most thermoplastic polymers are high-molecular-weight polymers whose chains associate through weak Van der Waals forces, stronger dipole-dipole interactions and hydrogen bonding. Thermoplastic polymers constitute a large range of plastic materials, such as polymethylmethacrylate (PMMA), cycloolefin copolymer (COC), and polycarbonate (PC).

Several molding processes are used for making thermoplastics microparts. The hot embossing and the microinjection molding seem to be the most suitable processes for industrially manufacturing. A detailed introduction will be available in the followed section.

3. Micro/nano Manufacturing of Thermoplastics-based Lab-on-a-chip

In the past two decades, there has been an explosion of interest in the field of lab-on-a-chip devices. Such devices have many advantages, including integration, miniaturization, automation, and reduced consumption of reagents. Recently, researchers have paid more attentions on thermoplastics-based lab-on-a-chip devices. There are mainly three advantages for it: (1) the cheap raw material; (2) the excellent availability of thermoplastics; (3) the simple fabrication process. In this section, an overview of the fabrication techniques for thermoplastics-based lab-on-a-chip devices will be provided.

3.1. Micro/nano Machining Process

3.1.1. Master Fabrication

For polymer replication techniques, the first thing is the fabrication of the master that presents the inverse structure of the desired polymer structure. Silicon and nickel are the commonly used materials for the master.

The fabrication of the silicon-based master is mainly based on photolithography and etching. The wet etching process results in a trapezoidal cross section with a wall angle of 54.7° for a silicon wafer with crystal orientation of <100>. In order to obtain high aspect ratio microstructures, the dry etching process is recommendable. As the silicon master is very thin and fragile, the silicon master was often bonded to another silicon wafer or a Pyrex glass to provide additional strength to the master and improve the lifetime [14, 15].

The fabrication of the nickel-based master involves an electroplating process. Firstly, the photoresist is patterned on a nickel plate. Secondly, the patterned photoresist is placed into a galvanic bath to electroplate. Thirdly, the photoresist is removed and the nickel-based master is polished. The substrate of the master could also be a silicon wafer [16], but a conducting metal seed layer should be deposited on the silicon wafer before coating the photoresist.

3.1.2. Hot Embossing

Hot embossing is a technique of imprinting microstructures on a thermoplastic substrate using a master mold [17]. The mold used to define the microstructures in the substrate can be made in a variety of ways including micromachining from metal, LIGA or UV-LIGA from silicon or metal, and laser fabrication. A wide variety of thermoplastics have been successfully hot embossed with and below micron-scale size features. Hot embossing have several advantages such as easy manufacturability, fast process, fabrication of high aspect ratio features, bio-compatible surfaces and low cost [18]. Usually hot embossing process includes four steps:

7) Heating substrate and mold above glass transition temperature (T_g) or close to viscous flow temperature (T_f).
8) Loading by pressing the mold on substrate.
9) Remaining the pressure and temperature for several minutes.
10) Cooling the mold & substrate and de-molding.

The first step can be performed isothermally or non-isothermally. Isothermal process, which is more popular, means polymer substrate and mold will be heated to same temperature. In contrast, non-isothermal process means that the substrate and the mold will be heated to different temperature [19]. T_g and T_f are two characteristic temperatures for thermoplastics. Below T_g, polymer will exhibit glassy state. At T_g <T< T_f, polymer will exhibit hyperelastic state. As temperature rise near or above T_f, polymer will exhibit viscous flow state.

The polymer flow and filling behavior as the polymer exhibits viscous flow state have been reported by several groups. Heyderman and Schift reported "dual-peak" [20] and "tri-peak" [21] filling behavior of molten PMMA film into micro-cavities during micro-embossing. The temperature used in their experiments was higher than T_g and close to T_f. These filling behaviors also have been found by Rowland et al. [22, 23].

Embossing near T_f. is usually used for the fabrication of thin film or nano features with female die. Many embossing process, such as the production of microfluidic device, have been conducted just slightly above T_g to replicate micro-structures into thick substrate. Juang et al. [24] investigated the filling behavior of thermoplastics into micro-cavities near glass transition temperature. The polymer exhibited a "single-peak" figure as deformed into the cavities. They also studied polymer deformation under a male die pressing. According to their report, there was a triangle-like region among the side wall of mold micro-protrusion, mold surface and substrate surface, which couldn't be filled completely during embossing.

Optimization of hot embossing parameters and processes has attracted more concerns. Many scholars investigated the relationship between hot embossing parameters and fabricated part quality. Lin et al. [25] reported their studies on the effects of pressure distributions during embossing. The results have shown more uniform shrinkage in the elastically deformed state during cooling. Worgull et al. [26] developed a simulation method for embossing process optimization and part design. They studied the effects of embossing and de-molding process on part quality. Chien et al. [27] studied the effects of embossing pressure and temperature on the replication precision of microchannel. They found the precision increase with the applied force until the associated dimensions reach saturated values, and embossing temperature shows similar influence on the precision. Shan et al. [28] studied the effects of embossing temperature on fidelity and global uniformity of microstructures. They found the formation of protrusive structures was not complete since there was little polymer flow at a temperature below T_g. However, the cavities are still well-filled.

Liu's group started to fabricate thermoplastic microfluidic device by hot embossing since 2000. We investigated the deformation and filling behavior of glassy or hyperelastic thermoplastics during hot embossing with male die [29]. We called the triangle-like region among the side wall of mold micro-protrusion, mold surface and substrate surface as "lack-filling region", and studied its formation process. Results show that the lack-filling region was generated, due to the plastic deformation and stress concentration near this region and that lack-filling formation was affected by applied temperature and pressure. We also established the relationship between hot embossing parameters and replication precision. By using optimal hot embossing process, we fabricated unifrom microchannels in PMMA, PET, COC and other. The fabricated channels are shown in Figure 3.1.

3.1.3. Micro-injection Molding

Micro-injection molding is a technique that offers mass-production capabilities with relatively low costs. Its other advantages include short-cycle times, the potential for full-automation, accurate replication and dimensional control as well as the existence of considerable know-how, transferable from conventional injection molding.

Kukla et al. [30] defined the meaning of micro-injection molding. Firstly, the weight of micro-injection molded part is used for a part weighting a few milligram. It can but need not have dimensions on micrometer scale. Secondly, an injection molded part with micro-structured regions is usually a part on a conventional scale, which is characterized by dimensions of the order of micrometer. Thirdly, a micro-precision part can have any dimensions, but has tolerances in the micrometer range.

Micro-injection molding is the process of transferring a thermoplastic material in the form of granules from a hopper into a heated barrel so that it becomes molten and soft. The material is then forced under pressure inside a mould cavity where it is subjected to holding pressure to compensate for material shrinkage. The material solidifies as the mould temperature decreases below the glass transition temperature of the polymer. After sufficient time, the material freezes into the mould shape and gets ejected, and the cycle is repeated. A typical cycle lasts in a range of few seconds to few minutes. The process has a set of advantages that makes it commercially applicable with potential for further developments in the future.

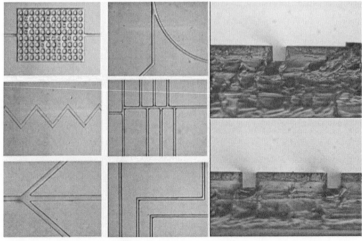

Figure 3.1. The photographs of fabricated microchannels.

3.1.4. Electrode Integration

To achieve the lab-on-a-chip device, the microelectrode is one of the essential components of microfluidic chips. The microelectrode has been used as driving, separating and detecting electrodes [31-33], heating elements and temperature sensors [34-36]. Electrode materials used include various forms of carbon and metal, such as carbon paste [37], carbon ink [38], carbon fiber [39], carbon film [40], platinum [41], gold [42], silver [43], palladium [44] and copper [45].

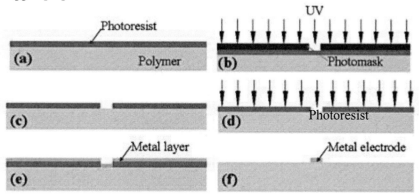

Figure 3.2. Process steps of the modified lift-off process. (a) Spin-coating of the photoresist; (b) First exposure of the photoresist; (c) Developing of the photoresist; (d) Second exposure of the photoresist; (e) Deposition of the metal layer; (f) Removing of the photoresist.

The fabrication process of carbon-based electrodes on polymer substrate was mainly composed of two steps: fabrication of the electrode channel and filling or placing of the electrode. The first example of the microelectrode as an electrochemical detector in polymer microfluidic chips employed carbon ink [38]. UV laser was used to ablate a 23-mm-long, 15~60-µm-deep and 30-µm-wide microchannel in a poly (ethylene terephthalate) (PET) substrate, then carbon ink was filled into the microchannel and cured to form the carbon microelectrode. Lunte et al. reported carbon fiber and carbon paste electrodes with PDMS-based chips [37, 39]. The electrode channel was fabricated in PDMS using cast molding method. The carbon fibers or carbon paste was subsequently placed into the electrode channel.

Metal microelectrodes included wire electrodes [46, 47] and thin-film electrodes [48, 49]. The fabrication method of wire electrodes was similar with that of carbon-based electrodes. Soper et al. embossed two electrode channels in PMMA substrate, and a pair of Pt wires (127 µm diameter) was placed into the channel for conductivity detection [36].

The thin-film metal microelectrodes are fabricated commonly using standard photolithography [31, 48, 50]. The fabrication process needs to be modified due to the big difference in temperature stability and resistance against chemicals between Si and polymers. The fabrication process reported can be divided into the lift-off process and the wet etching process.

The fabrication steps of the modified lift-off process are schematically shown in Figure 3.2 [31]: a) the photoresist is spin-coated on the polymer substrate; b) the photoresist is soft-baked and exposed to UV light through a photomask that contains the desired microelectrode features; c) the photoresist is developed; d) the substrate is secondly exposed to UV light without a photomask; e) a thin metal layer is deposited on the polymer substrate and f) the photoresist is removed by lift-off in 5% NaOH solution.

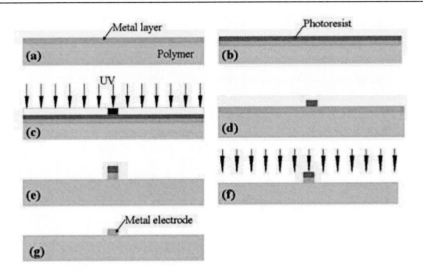

Figure 3.3. Process steps of the modified wet etching process. (a) Deposition of the metal layer; (b) spin-coating of the photoresist; (c) first exposure of the photoresist; (d) developing of the photoresist; (e) etching of the metal layer; (f) second exposure of the photoresist; (g) removing of residual photoresist.

Liu's group developed a modified wet etching process [50], as shown in Figure 3.3: a) a thin metal layer is deposited on the polymer substrate; b) a positive photoresist is spin-coated on the metal layer; c) the photoresist is soft-baked and exposed to UV light through a photomask; d) the photoresist is developed, and hard baked; e) the substrate is placed in a chemical solution to etch the exposed metal, f) after a rinse, the substrate is secondly exposed to UV light without a photomask and g) the substrate is placed in 0.5% NaOH solution to remove the residual photoresist.

Based on this process, a PMMA microfluidic chip with integrated Cu microelectrodes was fabricated and applied for the direct electrochemical detection of a glucose solution and amino acids [50, 51]. We also fabricated a PMMA chip with integrated Cu interdigitated microelectrode arrays for AC electroosmotic pump [52], as shown in Figure 3.4.

Besides the photolithography method, other methods were also reported. Soper's group developed a selective electroless metal plating method for the fabrication of thin-film metal microelectrodes on polymer substrates [53]. Evaporating with a mask containing the pattern of the electrode was also used to fabricate thin-film electrodes [42, 49].

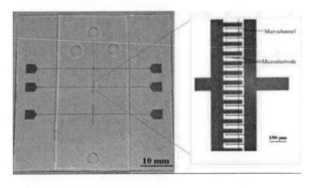

Figure 3.4. Photograph of the PMMA microfluidic chip with metal microelectrodes. Reproduced with permission from Elsevier.

3.1.5. Thermal Bonding

Microfluidic device generally contains closed channels. Chip bonding is used to form closed channels by bonding a cover plate onto the substrate. Sever kinds of chip bonding approaches, such as adhesive bonding [54], thermal bonding [55], solvent bonding [56], and localized heating assisted bonding [57], have been developed in the past decade. Adhesive bonding use glue to seal the substrate with a cover plate, which may cause channel clog and change channel side wall properties. Solvent bonding use chemical solvent to dissolve the surface layer of polymer substrate and cover plate, subsequently seal them by apply a small load. This approach may cause channel collapse during dissolve process. Localized heating uses laser, ultrasonic or induction to heat the region near channels and seal the chip only at the heated region. This approach usually needs expensive heating device or complicate assisted microstructures.

Thermal bonding is an appropriate mass-production approach for thermoplastics-based microchips. Its basic steps are as follows:

1) Heating substrate and cover plate close to T_g.
2) Applying load at a certain pressure.
3) Remaining the pressure and temperature for several minutes.
4) Cooling and de-molding.

The main problem in thermal bonding is the channel deformation generated at a bonding temperature near T_g. One solution is the surface modification that is an approach to modify polymer surface properties by solvent and plasma [58]. Enhanced surface properties can be served to decrease bonding temperature and pressure.

Electrophoresis microchip is a kind of well-known microfluidic device with integrated microelectrodes for chemical or biological sample detection. The fabrication of thermoplastic electrophoresis microchip by thermal bonding may be bothered by electrode fracture. Electrode fracture means that the metal electrode integrated on the substrate may generate cracks or completely fracture during thermal bonding process. Liu's group studied the mechanism of electrode fracture and successfully developed PMMA and PET electrophoresis microchips with intact electrodes for biological and chemical sample analysis [59, 60]. We found that several positions on the electrode is the most dangerous region to generate crack, and the factors including the part length of electrode in the reservior(L), electrode figure, bonding temperature and bonding pressure could affect the electrode stress at these regions. By enlarging reservoirs and decreasing bonding temperature, we fabricated thermoplastic microchips with intact on-chip electrodes. The fabricated chips have been used to detect dopamine, catechol and glucose.

Thermoplastic microfluidic device with three-dimensional structures in its channels has attracted more concerns in recent years. To fabricate this kind of device by thermal bonding, the problem of channel deformation has to be overcome. One solution is to decrease the bonding temperature and pressure. Liu's group developed a PMMA device with three-dimensional in-channel microstructures for blood cells filtration [61]. This device used cross-flow filtration pathway to separate white blood cells (WBCs) from red blood cells (RBCs), the in-channel structures and whole channel networks were shown in Figure 3.5. Two parallel microwires have been fabricated at both side of the main channel. There is a microgap between the top of microweir and the cover plate, which allows RBCs to pass and obstructs

WBCs. The size of microgap is only 3~8 microns which match the size of mammal RBCs. A difficulty for the fabrication of this device is to keep the microgap in its appropriate size. If the device is thermal bonded at 95°C~100°C, the microgap will be readily clogged due to channel deformation.

Liu's group presented a method composed of structure design compensation and plasma surface treatment to minimize channel deformation. The deformation of microchannels during thermal bonding is estimated, and then the structure compensation of deformation will be quantitatively considered. Plasma surface treatment means the use of low temperature oxygen plasma to modify the surface of PMMA substrates. The treated substrates can be bonded at a relative low temperature to reduce channel deformation. By using these methods, a PMMA filtration device with five microns microgaps was fabricated.

Multilayer microfluidic device is another hot topic. Liu's group investigated the fabrication process of thermoplastic multilayer microchip and developed an eight-layer micromixer and a seven-layer micro dilution device [62]. An CO_2 laser is used to engrave the microchannels in PMMA substrates. The channels in different layers connect with each other by through holes to form a three-dimensional channel network. Low temperature oxygen plasma treatment was used to improve the surface properties of PMMA substrates. The treated substrates were bonded at 85°C to reduce channel deformation. The fabricated micro devices, which have been shown in Figure 3.6, were used to achieve three-dimensional mixing and dilution of chemical samples.

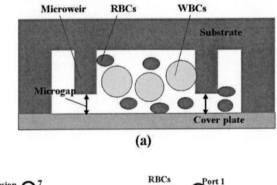

(a)

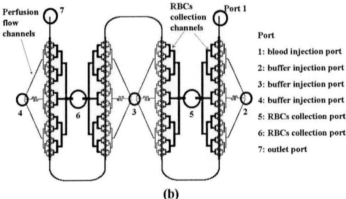

(b)

Figure 3.5. The microfluidic device for blood cells filtration. Reproduced with permission from IOP. (a) The in-channel microstructures; (b) the whole channel networks.

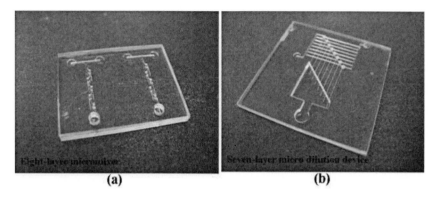

(a)   (b)

Figure 3.6. The multilayer PMMA microfluidic devices. Reproduced with permission from Elsevier. (a) The eight-layer PMMA micromixer; (b) the seven-layer micro dilution device.

3.2. Automatic Manufacturing Equipment

Hot embossing machines are used to fabricate microstructures in thermoplastics substrates or to seal a substrate with a cover plate by heating and loading. It is significant for the volume production of thermoplastic microfluidic chips. Several kinds of hot embossing machines have been developed in the past two decades.

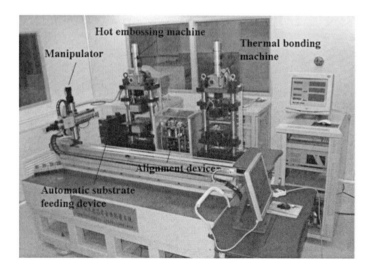

Figure 3.7. The thermoplastic chip automatic fabrication system.

A series of hot embossing machines had been developed by Jenoptik Corporation. HEX series machines could work manually, semi-automatically and automatically. Their embossing pressure and temperature can increase above 200KN and 500°C, respectively. EV510HE and EV520HE were developed by Austria EVG Corporation. They were both semi-automatic embossing system. The hot embossing system was configured with a universal embossing chamber, high-vacuum and high-contact force capabilities and manages the whole range of polymers suitable for hot embossing.

Liu et al developed a thermoplastics microchip automatic fabrication system (RYJ-I) in 2003. This system composed of hot embossing machine, alignment device for aligning the position of substrate and cover plate, feeding device for automatic substrate feeding, manipulator for automatic substrates feeding or discharging and thermal bonding machine. Figure 3.7 is the photography of this fabrication system. The thermal bonding machine is similar to the hot embossing one. It consisted of a DC torque motor, a screw, two press heads, a linear encoder and a control system. Four Thermal Electric Cooler blocks were placed into the press heads for heating and cooling. The DC torque motor could provide a constant force with a control resolution of 0.5 N. A beam load cell was placed under the lower press head to measure the force. A linear encoder was mounted on the movable plate to monitor the displacement of the upper press head. All the process can be controlled by a computer.

4. DEVELOPMENT OF LIQUID-FEED MICRO DIRECT METHANOL FUEL CELLS ON SILICON SUBSTRATE AND METAL FOIL USING MICROFABRICATION

4.1. Introduction

In the past decade, with the help of micro/nano fabrication techniques, a number of micro- or mini- devices had been made successfully. More recently, in order to satisfy the needs of more compact designs of these devices, integrated micro systems that consist of MEMS-based devices, IC and on-chip power sources also have been developed [63]. However, the limited energy density of the micro power sources has become one of the major obstacles for a further progress of the micro systems. In order to solve these problems, a few kinds of micro or miniature power sources had been developed. In 1995, Lee et al. [64] presented a hydrogenated amorphous silicon solar cell array as an on-board power source for electrostatic micro systems. Subsequently, more competitive micro power sources such as proton-exchange- membrane (PEM) based micro fuel cell [65-66] and nuclear micro-battery [67] were developed to meet different power demands over the last couple of years. Among those micro power sources reported, micro fuel cell is one of the most promising power sources for micro systems and other miniature portable devices because of its high energy density, high energy conversion efficiency, environmentally benign emission and applicability under various conditions. In addition, as a micro power source combined with micro fabrication and electrochemical technologies, micro PEM fuel cell has good processing compatibility with the integrated micro systems.

It is well known that PEM fuel cell can be fueled with hydrogen [65, 68-71], methanol [66, 72-77], ethanol [78-81], formic acid [82-25] and dimethylether [86], etc. However, the fuel for a micro PEM fuel cell should meet multiple demands such as high energy density, electrochemical activity, inexpensive source, convenient storage and easy management in fuel cell system. Therefore, those fuel cells using liquid fuel directly instead of gaseous fuel will be more suitable for a micro/miniature system design because of the eliminating of the requirement for onboard hydrogen storage and fuel reforming. This feature will also have the potential for low-volume and lightweight packaging of the micro fuel cell system. Within the last decade, tremendous effort has been made to the development of liquid-feed micro direct methanol fuel cell (μDMFC) as a micro/miniature power source candidate. The direct use of liquid methanol in micro fuel cell offers considerable attractions from the points of the view of simplicity of design, easy miniaturization, and the system low cost.

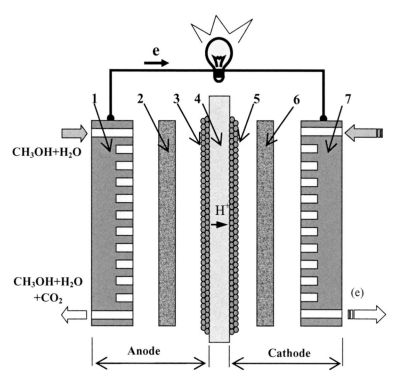

Figure 4.1. Schematic of a liquid-feed direct methanol fuel cell: 1-anode polar plate, 2-anode diffusion layer, 3-anode catalyst layer, 4-proton-exchange-membrane, 5-cathode catalyst layer, 6-cathode diffusion layer, 7-cathode polar plate.

As shown in Figure 4.1, a liquid-feed DMFC can be divided into seven segments. The two outer segments are polar plates with flow channels for reactants and products to enter and exit the cell, respectively. On the other hand, the polar plates are also functioned as current collectors to collect the electrons. The adjacent segments are electronically conducting diffusion layers that allow even distribution of reactants diffuse to the anode and cathode. The diffusion layers are produced by carbon paper, which is hydrophilic in anode side and hydrophobic in cathode side. The central part of the fuel cell is a piece of membrane-electrode-assembly (MEA), which is formed by coating anode and cathode catalysis layer on different sides of the PEM. The catalyst in anode and cathode is PtRu/C and Pt/C, respectively.

The working performance of a liquid-feed DMFC is related to a typical electrochemical reaction enhanced by catalysis. When the aqueous methanol solution is fed into the anode, the methanol reacts electrochemically with water in active sides of the catalyst nano particles to produce electrons, protons and carbon dioxide. While the electrons are forced to flow through the external circuit to form the current and the protons transport through the PEM. The protons combine with oxygen and electrons from the external circuit to form water in the cathode. The whole procedure of this reaction can be described as follows:

Anode: $CH_3OH + H_2O \xrightarrow{\quad PtRu/C \quad} CO_2 + 6H^+ + 6e^-$ (1)

Cathode: $6H^+ + 6e^- + \dfrac{3}{2}O_2 \xrightarrow{\quad Pt/C \quad} 3H_2O$ (2)

Overall reaction: $CH_3OH + \dfrac{3}{2}O_2 \rightarrow 2H_2O + CO_2$ (3)

For a liquid-feed μDMFC, the preparation of the above-mentioned segments is quite different from those of large-dimension DMFCs due to manufacturing limitation. For example, although most of the conventional MEAs made by thin-film deposition techniques also can be used in μDMFC due to their thin outer shape (100~300μm in thickness), the manufacturing of the polar plates are different. For traditional DMFC, the flow-field channels on polar plate usually can be milled on graphite or metal plates. However, it is difficult to mill the channels less than 1mm in hydraulic diameter on the μDMFC polar plate. Therefore, microfabrication is a better choice with the advantages of fine feature resolution, good repeatability, easy batch production and integrated process sequences [87]. In the most concerned literatures, researchers mainly focused on the micro-machining of the μDMFC flow-field plates utilizing silicon [66, 88-90], polymer [91-92] and metal foil [93-95]. Subsequently, bulk micromachining on silicon, UV-LIGA-based hot embossing on polymer and micro wet chemical etching on metal foil can be employed to the microfabrication of the μDMFC polar plate.

4.2. Silicon Micromachining for μDMFC

To make the μDMFC polar plate on a silicon substrate, typically wet etching [88-90] and deep reactive ion etching (DRIE) [66] can be used. One of the distinct advantages of the DRIE is the ability of easily obtaining silicon structure with high aspect ratio (depth/width) and straight sidewalls. However, consider to the fact that most of the μDMFC flow fields can be formed by channels with aspect ratio less than 1, silicon wet etching using hot KOH or tetramethylammonium hydroxide (TMAH) solution is more simple and convenient. Therefore, the manufacturing process of μDMFC polar plate using silicon bulk micromachining by KOH wet etching is mainly discussed in this section.

4.2.1. Design of the Silicon μDMFC Demonstrator

To illustrate the micromachining process of the silicon flow field, a liquid-feed, air-breathing μDMFC demonstrator was designed [96]. As shown in Figure 4.1, the demonstrator runs on aqueous methanol solution in anode and absorbs oxygen from the ambient using air-breathing mechanism in cathode. The features of liquid-feed and air-breathing can help to deal with the problems of reactants delivery and management in fuel cell under miniature scale working conditions.

The structure of the polar plates is illustrated in Figure 4.2. In anode flow field, 400μm wide serpentine microchannels with three parallel partial cross-sections are adopted to lead the methanol solution into the reaction zone and guide the byproducts produced in the electrochemical reaction from the reaction place. In cathode flow field, a 11×11 matrix of micro through holes are made to form air-breathing flow field that can absorb oxygen from convectional air and let out the water vapor to prevent flooding in cathode. The dimension of each breathing hole is 400μm×400μm and the effective area of the air-breathing flow field is in accordance with the MEA active area which is 8mm×8mm in this demonstrator. At the edge of the polar plates, 8 packaging slots with a width of 500μm is designed to form a rivet-like structure using cured epoxy resin to package the μDMFC. The dimension of each polar plate is 16.5×16.5×0.38mm, which means that a piece of 2 inch silicon wafer would be suitable for the production of 4 polar plates in a parallel silicon microfabrication process.

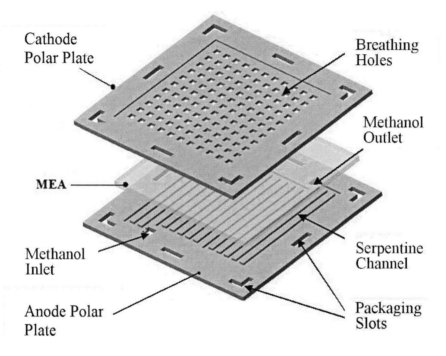

Figure 4.2. Schematic of a liquid-feed, air breathing μDMFC demonstrator[96]. Reproduced with permission from TRANS TECH.

4.2.2. Microfabrication of Silicon Polar Plates

The major microfabrication processes of the silicon polar plates are shown in Figure 4.3. The raw material for the production of polar plates was 380μm thick, 2 inch, N-type, <100> oriented double-side polished silicon wafers with a resistivity lower than 0.05Ω·cm.

Firstly, 1μm thick SiO_2 layer thermal oxide was formed as mask for subsequent silicon wet etching. Then the wafers were spin-coated with a layer of photoresist on backside, and the packaging slots, inlet/outlet in anode and breathing-hole matrix in cathode were patterned by first photolithography. Secondly, the exposed SiO_2 was removed by buffered oxide etching (BOE) and the wafer was then etched in a hot KOH solution (40Wt %, 90°C). Subsequently, the micro channels and breathing-hole matrix on front side of the wafer were patterned and developed with an infrared-ray-based, double-sided alignment photolithography. The front side of wafer was then etched using the same steps mentioned above to form the flow field. Finally, Cu/Pt layers acted as current collectors were sputtered onto the front side of the wafer with titanium as adhesive layer. The SEM images of the silicon polar plates are shown in Figure 4.4.

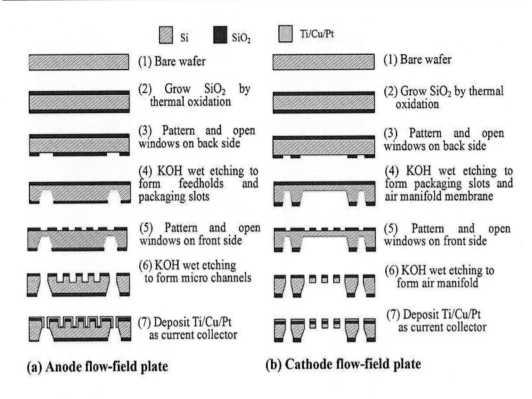

Figure 4.3. Fabrication processes of the silicon polar plates[96]. Reproduced with permission from TRANS TECH.

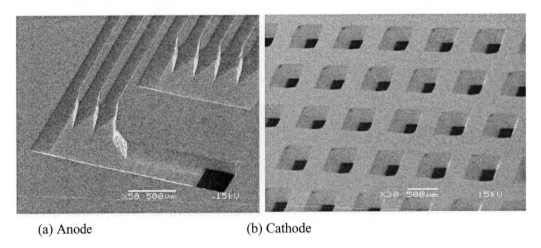

(a) Anode   (b) Cathode

Figure 4.4. SEM images of the flow field plates[96]. Reproduced with permission from TRANS TECH.

4.2.3. Packaging and Test of the Silicon µDMFC

The silicon µDMFC demonstrator in this section was packaged by filling epoxy resin into the packaging slots in polar plates and curing the fuel cell at 60℃ for 5 hours in an oven. Figure 4.5 is the packaging configurations, which shows that the cured epoxy resin can form a riveting structure by using the packaging slots with the taper cross section that naturally formed from the <100> oriented silicon wafer during the wet etching process. The shrinkage and adhesion effects of the epoxy resin during cure provide clamping force to the μDMFC. After the fuel cell was packaged, polypropylene (PP) tubes with an inner diameter of 500μm were connected to the inlet and outlet of the anode flow field by using epoxy resign. A core shaft was used in this process to provide an anchor point and a rigid support for the PP tube before the epoxy resin was cured.

The packaged μDMFC is shown in Figure 4.6. The outside dimension of the packaged one is 15×15×1.2mm. Figure 4.6 also shows the fuel cell under performance evaluation by connecting the inlet tube of the anode flow field to a syringe pump. The cathode breathing holes is opened to the ambient during this process.

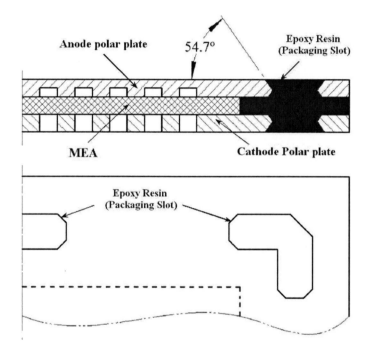

Figure 4.5. Schematic diagram of the packaging configuration [96]. Reproduced with permission from TRANS TECH.

In order to evaluate the performance of the silicon μDMFC demonstrator, an electrochemical polarization analysis was employed. The polarization curves of the fuel cell were obtained using a programmable electronic load which can simulate the variation of the external load during the test. The experiments were conducted by changing the concentration and temperature of the methanol solution fed to the anode flow field. Due to the very small MEA active area (8mm×8mm) was adopted, the μDMFC performance in this study was not sensitive to the change of methanol flow rate which fell in an ordinary capability range of a syringe pump. Therefore, a fixed methanol flow rate of 0.1ml/min was used in the test. Meanwhile, the operating conditions of the fuel cell cathode were kept unchanged during the evaluations. Diluted methanol solution (1M~4M) was used in order to avoid the penetration of the methanol through the Nafion® membrane, which will lead to a serious power loss of the μDMFC. The methanol solution was preheated to 60℃ before it was used in the fuel cell. After the methanol solution was fed into the μDMFC anode and humidified for 1~2 minutes, the open circuit potential of the single-cell μDMFC demonstrator was about 0.70V. Figure 4.7 compares the performance of the fuel cell under different methanol concentration. The results shows that peak power density of the fuel cell was increased from 5.8 mW·cm^{-2} to 8 mW·cm^{-2} with the 1M and 2M methanol solution. However, the peak power density decreased to 7.4 mW·cm^{-2} and 6.5mW·cm^{-2} when the methanol concentration was increased to 3M and 4M, respectively. 2M methanol solution yields a better performance, which is mainly due to the better compromise between the methanol crossover and mass transportation during the operation.

Figure 4.6. The packaged μDMFC under testing [96]. Reproduced with permission from TRANS TECH.

4.3. Micro Photochemical Etching (μPCE) of the Stainless Steel Polar Plates

Recently, a number of micro fuel cells were fabricated on silicon substrates. However, there are two problems in the silicon micro fuel cells. Firstly, silicon is quite fragile, which makes it is difficult to seal the fuel cell tightly with low contact resistance between MEA and polar plates. Secondly, silicon is nearly electrically insulated, which need a metal thin film deposited on its flow field surface to collect the current. Therefore, the cost will be significantly increased when the fuel cell resistance is minimized.

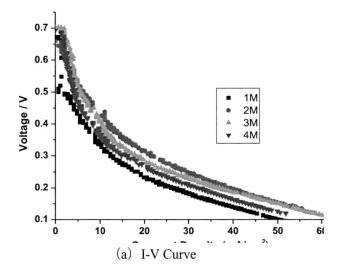

(a) I-V Curve

Figure 4.7. (Continued).

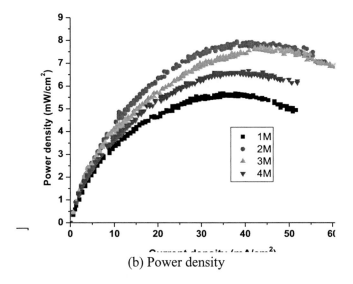

(b) Power density

Figure 4.7. Si-based µDMFC performance with different methanol concentrations [96]. Reproduced with permission from TRANS TECH.

An alternative method is to fabricate the polar plates on stainless steel foil using µPCE. Stainless steel foil has much higher conductivity, mechanical strength and ability of corrosion-resistance. µPCE is a high-quality and low-cost method for machining flat metal parts.

4.3.1. Fundamental of µPCE Accuracy Control

Recently, µPCE has been widely used to fabricate precise stainless steel parts, such as heat exchangers, photo-electricity encoder, polar plates of fuel cell [63-66]. This technique employs chemical etchant to remove unwanted work piece materials through a photoresist stencil [63]. Ferric salts (ferric chloride and ferric nitrate) mixed with inorganic acids (hydrochloric acid and nitric acid) serves as a relatively cheap and productive etchant for stainless steel etching. As an isotropic etching, the etching topography of stainless steel parts is mainly determined by three parameters: initial stencil width, etching depth and undercut. Generally, the initial stencil width should closely match the line width of the mask [67], while the etching depth and the undercut can be controlled by the etching time. In order to improve the precision of the engineering components and devices, dimensional compensations in mask design should be made and the etching time needs to be accurately estimated and controlled.

The etching rate is a differential form of the distance at vertical or horizontal direction. The accurate estimation of the etching rate is the precondition to ensure precession control of the PCE process. Unfortunately, the etching rate is found to have a nonlinear relation with the stencil width and etching time. Allen [67] attributed this problem to the difficulty of replacing a spent etchant with fresh solution at the bottom of narrow slots. Masato et al [69] used a modified diffusion model to simulate the etching topography when the initial stencil width ranged from 1μm to 3μm.

4.3.2. Experiments

Liu's group has researched on the μPCE etching experimentally with different initial stencil widths (from 50μm to 350μm) [97]. Before etching each sheet (SS316L 0.4mm thick) was first degreased with acetone in an ultrasonic bath for 5 minutes, then cleaned with alcohol and finally rinsed with de-ionized water. After being preheated in an oven at 110±1℃ for 20mins, the stainless steel sheet was spin coated with negative photoresist, and 10μm thickness was obtained. The steel sheet was exposed using UV lithography process, and then the pattern was developed in 1% sodium carbonate solution and dried at 95±0.5℃ on a hot plate for 5 minutes. Each sheet was etched in a spray etcher at 30℃. After etching, the photoresist was removed in 5% NaOH solution at 50℃. Figure 4.8 shows a stainless steel foil with nine etched slots which have different initial stencil width before etching. All the slots were 4mm in length with 1~1.5 mm pitches between two adjacent slots. Each sheet was etched under different etching time.

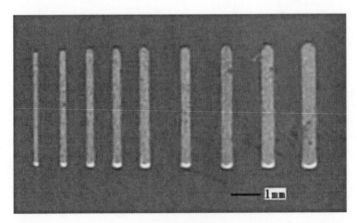

Figure 4.8. The photograph of the etched slots [97]. Reproduced with permission from IOP.

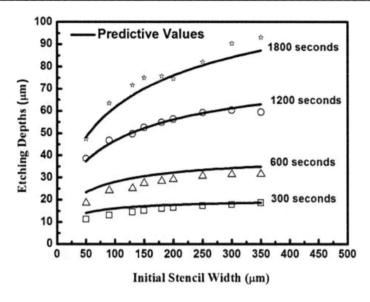

Figure 4.9. The effects of the initial stencil width on the etching depth [97]. Reproduced with permission from IOP.

Figure 4.9 shows the relationship between the etching depth and the initial stencil width under different etching times. The predictive results from theoretical calculation are compared with those from the experiment. Results show that the predictive results match the experimental values well at the etching time of 1200s and 1800s. It also can be seen that the numerical values at the etching time of 300s and 600s are a little higher than the experimental values. As illustrated in Figure 4.9, the etching depth increases with the increase of initial stencil width at the initial region at a fixed etching time, and the etching depth finally approaches to a constant.

4.3.3. Fabricate μDMFC with Taper Flow Channel Using μPCE

With the significant decreasing of feature sizes of the anode flow channels in μDMFC, CO_2 clogging may become a vital limitation for further improvement of the fuel cell performance. It is even more difficult to remove the CO_2 bubbles from micro channels with hydraulic diameter of 1mm or less in μDMFC. In this work, we developed a μDMFC using newly designed anode flow field pattern with gradual change in width along the micro channel [98]. We call this type of flow field as non-equipotent flow field (NEFF) in order to distinguish it from the conventional flow field patterns. The flow channels were fabricated on stainless foil using μPCE technique. In order to accurately control the channel dimensions during the photochemical etching, the above described scale effect model was used to calculate the mask compensation. Transparent μDMFC single cells with and without this flow field pattern were fabricated and comparatively studied. Results shows that the performance of liquid-feed μDMFC was effectively promoted using the designing concept of non-equipotent flow field, which is due to the alleviation of the CO_2 block in anode flow channel.

The structure of a single cell μDMFC in this experiment is shown in Figure 4.10. The anode and cathode flow field patterns of the fuel cell are serpentine channel and dot-matrix air-breathing holes, respectively. In order to observe the two phase liquid- gas behavior in the flow field during the electrochemical reaction, transparent enclosures produced using PMMA sheet material were used in the experiment.

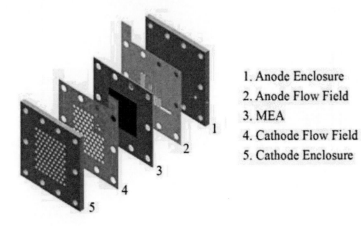

1. Anode Enclosure
2. Anode Flow Field
3. MEA
4. Cathode Flow Field
5. Cathode Enclosure

Figure 4.10. Schematic structure of the liquid-feed μDMFC [98]. Reproduced with permission from MDPI.

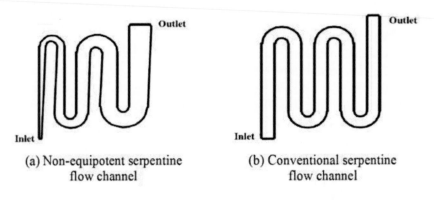

(a) Non-equipotent serpentine flow channel

(b) Conventional serpentine flow channel

Figure 4.11. Flow channel patterns [98]. Reproduced with permission from MDPI.

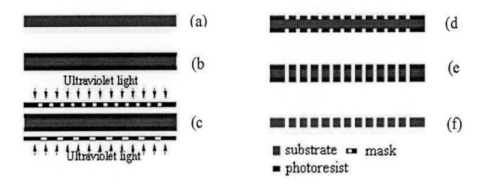

Figure 4.12. μPCE processes of the stainless steel flow channels [98]. Reproduced with permission from MDPI.

The flow pattern of the Non-equipotent serpentine flow channel and the conventional serpentine flow channel is shown in Figure 4.11.The flow channels with the smallest channel dimension of 400µm were fabricated by using double-sides micro photochemical etching. The fabrication sequence is shown in Figure 4.12. Firstly, the SS316L substrate was cleaned and dried (a), and then spin-coating and soft-baking process were applied to form 10µm thick photoresist layers on both sides of the substrate (b). Secondly, the flow field patterns on the mask were transferred to the photoresist layers using UV-based lithography techniques (c). subsequently a hard-baking step after the patterns were developed in a 1% sodium carbonate developer (d). Finally, the stainless steel substrates were immersed in FeCl$_3$-HCl based etchant (e). After the micro channels was etched to the desire dimensions, the photoresist layer on the flow field plates was removed by using hot concentrated NaOH solution.

Figure 4.13 shows the schematic drawing for the test of µDMFC with different flow channel. A high accuracy syringe pump is used to deliver methanol solution to the µDMFC. An electronic load is adopted to simulate the variation of the external load during the test. The inlet-to-outlet pressure drop in anode flow field is monitored by a pressure transmitter. The CCD camera is adopted to record the flow images. The experimental data and images are acquired and treated with a real-time connecting computer.

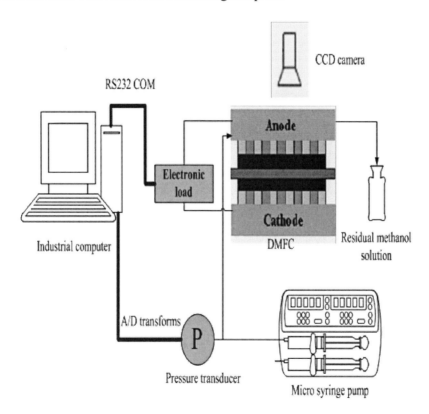

Figure 4.13. Schematic of the µDMFC test loop [98]. Reproduced with permission from MDPI.

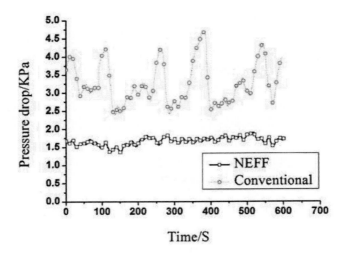

Figure 4.14. Pressure drops in conventional and NEFF channels [98]. Reproduced with permission from MDPI.

Figure 4.14 shows the time-history curves of the inlet-to-outlet pressure drops in the conventional and NEFF flow channels. The pressure drops are measured at an output current of 100mA of the fuel cell. It can be seen from Figure 4.15 that the pressure drops in the conventional flow channel is much higher than that in the NEFF channel. On the other hand, the amplitude and frequency of the pressure drop curves, reflecting the periodical accumulation and elimination of the CO_2 bubbles in the micro channels, also present different feature at the same fuel cell current. The fluctuation of the pressure drop in the NEFF flow channel is also much lower than that in the conventional one. It can be concluded that the non-equipotent design of the µDMFC anode flow field effectively mitigate the CO_2 clogging in the anode flow channels. Figure 4.15 compares the µDMFC performance under NEFF and conventional flow channels using 3M methanol solution at a flow rate of 3ml/h (temperature is 25°C). Results shows that performance of µDMFC was effectively promoted using the design of non-equipotent flow field, due to the alleviation of the CO_2 block in anode flow channel.

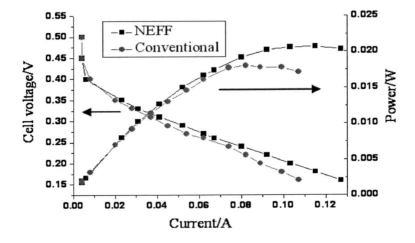

Figure 4.15. Performance of the µDMFC with conventional and NEFF flow channels [98]. Reproduced with permission from MDPI.

REFERENCES

[1]   L. J. Guo, X. Cheng, C. F. Chou.(2004). Fabrication of Size-Controllable Nanofluidic Channels by Nanoimprinting and Its Application for DNA Stretching. *Nano Letters, 4,* 69-73.

[2]   Y. C. Wang, A Stevens, J Han. (2005). Million-fold preconcentration of proteins and peptides by nanofluidic filter. *Anal. Chem., 77,* 4293-4299.

[3]   Rohit Karnik, Rong Fan, Min Yue, et al. (2005). Electrostatic Control of Ions and Molecules in Nanofluidic Transistors. *Nano Letters, 5,* 943-948.

[4]   Hessel. V, H. Lowe F. Schonfeld, (2005) Micromixers - a review on passive and active mixing principles. Chemical Engineering Science, 60, 2479-2501.

[5]   D. Gobby, P. Angeli and A. Gavriilidis. (2001). Mixing characteristics of T-type microfluidic mixers. *J. Micromech. Microeng., 11,* 126-132.

[6]   Volker Hessel, Holger Lowe and Friedhelm Schonfeld. (2005). Micromixers—a review on passive and active mixing principles. *Chemical Engineering Science, 60,* 2479-2501.

[7]   N. T. Nguyen and Z. G. Wu. (2005). Micromixers—a review. *J. Micromech. Microeng., 15,* R1-R16.

[8]   Jeffrey T. Coleman and David Sinton. (2005). A sequential injection microfluidic mixing strategy. *Microfluid Nanofluid, 1,* 319-327.

[9]   Brian D. Iverson, Suresh V. Garimella. (2008). Recent advances in microscale pumping technologies: a review and evaluation. *Microfluid Nanofluid, 5,* 145-174.

[10] W. Y. Sim, H. J. Yoon, O. C. Jeong, et al. (2003).A phase-change type micropump with aluminum flap valves. *J. Micromech. Microeng., 13,* 286-294.

[11] Kwang W Oh and Chong H Ahn. (2006). A review of microvalves. *J. Micromech. Microeng., 16,* R13-R39.

[12] P. Sethu and C. H. Mastrangelo. (2004). Low Reynolds number flow through nozzle-diffuser elements in valveless micropumps. *Sensors and Actuators A: Physical, 113,* 226-235.

[13] H. Cho, H. Y. Kim, et al. (2004). Capillary passive valve in microfluidic systems. *NSTI-Nanotech, 1,* 263-266.

[14] J. Xu, L. Locascio, M. Gaitan, et al. (2000). Room-temperature imprinting method for plastic microchannel fabrication. *Anal. Chem., 72,* 1930-1933.

[15] J. S. Liu, C. Liu, J. H. Guo, et al. (2006). Electrostatic bonding of a silicon master to a glass wafer for plastic microchannel fabrication. *J. Mater. Process. Technol., 178,* 278-282.

[16] H. Becker and U. Heim. (2000). Hot embossing as a method for the fabrication of polymer high aspect ratio structures. *Sensors and Actuators A: Physical, 83,* 130-135.

[17] M. Heckele, W. Bacher, K.D. Muller. (1998). Hot embossing-The molding technique for plastic microstructures. *Microsystem Technologies, 4,* 122-124.

[18] Becker H and Gartner C. (2000). Polymer microfabrication methods for microfluidic analytical applications. *Electrophoresis, 21,* 12-26.

[19] Juang, Yi-Je, Lee. L. James, et al. (2002). Hot embossing in microfabrication. Part I Experimental. *Polymer Engineering and Science, 42,* 539-550.

[20] L. J. Heyderman, H. Schift, D. David, et al. (2000). Flow behavior of thin polymer films used for hot embossing lithography. *Microelectronic Engineering, 54,* 229-245.

[21] H Schift, L J Heyderman and Maur MAD. (2001). Pattern formation in hot embossing of thin polymer films. *Nanotechnology, 12,* 173-177.

[22] Harry D Rowland and King W. P. (2004). Polymer deformation and filling modes during microembossing. *J. Micromech. Microeng., 14,* 1625-1632.

[23] Harry D Rowland, Amy C Sun, P Randy Schunk, et al. (2005). Impact of polymer film thickness and cavity size on polymer flow during embossing: toward process design rules for nanoimprint lithography. *J. Micromech. Microeng., 15,* 2414-2425.

[24] Juang Y-J, Lee L J, et al. (2002). Hot embossing in microfabrication: Part II. Rheological characterization and process analysis. *Poly. Eng. Sci., 42,* 551-566.

[25] C. R. Lin, R. H. Chen and C. Hung. (2003). Preventing non-uniform shrinkage in open-die hot embossing of PMMA microstructures. *Journal of Materials Processing Technology, 140,* 173-178.

[26] M. Worgull, M. Heckele. (2004). New aspects of simulation in hot embossing. *Microsystem Technologies, 10,* 432-437.

[27] Chien R. D. (2006). Hot embossing of microfluidic platform. *International Communications in Heat and Mass Transfer, 33,* 645–653.

[28] Xue chuan Shan, Y. C. Liu, Y. C. Lam. (2008). Studies of polymer deformation and recovery in micro hot embossing. *Microsyst Technol, 14,* 1055-1060.

[29] C. Liu, J.M. Li, J.S. Liu, et al. Deformation behavior of solid polymer during hot embossing process. *Microelectronic Engineering,* Article in Press.

[30] C. Kukla, H. Loibl, H. Detter, et al. (1998). Micro-injection moulding: the aims of a project partnership. *Kunstsoffe-Plast Europe, 88,* 6-7.

[31] Grass B., Neyer A., et al. (2001). A new PMMA-microchip device for isotachophoresis with integrated conductivity detector. *Sensors and Actuators B: Chemical, 72,* 249-258.

[32] J. S. Ko, H. C. Yoon, H. Yang, et al. (2003). A polymer-based microfluidic device for immunosensing biochips. *Lab Chip, 3,* 106-133.

[33] Virdi G. S., Chutani R. K., Rao P. K., et al. (2008). Fabrication of low cost integrated micro-capillary electrophoresis analytical chip for chemical analysis. *Sensors and Actuators B: Chemical, 128,* 422-426.

[34] T. Yamamoto, T. Nojima, T. Fujii, et al. (2002). PDMS-glass hybrid microreactor array with embedded temperature control device. Application to cell-free protein synthesis. *Lab Chip, 2,* 197-202.

[35] T. M. Hsieh, C. H. Luo, F. C. Huang, et al. (2008). Enhancement of thermal uniformity for a microthermal cycler and its application for polymerase chain reaction, *Sensors and Actuators B: Chemical, 130,* 848-856.

[36] Yeung Stephen S. W., Lee Thomas M. H. and Hsing I. M. (2008). Electrochemistry-based real-time PCR on a microchip. *Anal. Chem., 80,* 363-368.

[37] R. S. Martin, A. J. Gawron, B. A. Fogarty, et al. (2001). Carbon paste-based electrochemical detectors for microchip capillary electrophoresis/electrochemistry. *Analyst, 126,* 277-280.

[38] J. S. Rossier, M. A. Roberts, R. Ferrigno, et al. (1999), Electrochemical detection in polymer microchannels. *Anal. Chem., 71,* 4294-4299.

[39] R. S. Martin, K. L. Ratzlaff, B. H. Huynh, et al. (2002). In-channel electrochemical detection for microchip capillary electrophoresis using an electrically isolated potentiostat. *Anal. Chem., 74,* 1136-1143.

[40] N. E. Hebert, B. Snyder, R. L. McCreery, et al. (2003). Performance of pyrolyzed photoresist carbon films in a microchip capillary electrophoresis device with sinusoidal voltammetric detection. *Anal. Chem., 75,* 4265-4271.

[41] J. A. Lapos, D. P. Manica and A. G. Ewing. (2002). Dual fluorescence and electrochemical detection on an electrophoresis microchip. *Anal. Chem., 74,* 3348-3353.

[42] A. Hilmi and J. H. T. Luong. (2000). Electrochemical detectors prepared by electroless deposition for microfabricated electrophoresis chips. *Anal. Chem., 72,* 4677-4682.

[43] Yan J L, Yang X R and Wang E K. (2005). Electrochemical detection of anions on an electrophoresis microchip with integrated silver electrode. *Electroanalysis, 171,* 1222-1226.

[44] Lacher N. A., Lunte S. M. and Martin R. S. (2004). Development of a microfabricated palladium decoupler/electrochemical detector for microchip capillary electrophoresis using a hybrid glass/poly (dimethylsiloxane) device. *Anal. Chem., 76,* 2482-2491.

[45] Y. H. Dou, N. Bao, J. J. Xu, et al. (2004). Separation of proteins on surface-modified poly(dimethylsiloxane) microfluidic devices. *Electrophoresis, 25,* 3024-3031.

[46] M. Galloway, W. Stryjewski, A. Henry, et al. (2002). Contact conductivity detection in poly (methyl methacylate)-based microfluidic devices for analysis of mono-and polyanionic molecules. *Anal. Chem., 74,* 2407-2415.

[47] C. D. Garcia, G. Engling, P. Herckes, et al. (2005). Determination of levoglucosan from smoke samples using microchip capillary electrophoresis with pulsed amperometric detection. *Environ. Sci. Technol., 39,* 618-623.

[48] K. Ueno, F. Kitagawa, H. B. Kim, et al. (2000). Fabrication and characteristic responses of integrated microelectrodes in polymer channel chip. *Chemistry Letters, 8,* 858-859.

[49] D. Chen, F. L. Hsu, D. Z. Zhan, et al. (2001). Palladium film decoupler for amperometric detection in electrophoresis chips. *Anal. Chem., 73,* 758-762.

[50] J. S. Liu, Y. Luo, Y. Du, et al. (2005). Fabrication of polymethyl methacrylate electrophoresis chips with integrated copper electrodes. *Chinese Journal of Analytical Chemistry, 33,* 588-590.

[51] Y. Du, J. L. Yan, J. S. Liu, et al. (2005). Detection of amino acids on polymethyl methacrylate capillary electrophoresis chip. *Chinese Journal of Analytical Chemistry, 33,* 591-594.

[52] J. S. Liu, H. C. Qiao, C. Liu, et al. (2009). Plasma assisted thermal bonding for PMMA microfluidic chips with integrated metal microelectrodes. *Sensors and Actuators B: Chemical, 141,* 646-651.

[53] R. L. McCarley, B. Vaidya, S. Wei, et al. (2005). Resist-free patterning of surface architectures in polymer-based microanalytical devices. *J. Am. Chem. Soc., 127,* 842-843.

[54] Martin P. and Matson D. (1998). Fabrication of plastic microfluidic components. *Proc. SPIE Microfluidic Devices, 3515,* 172-176.

[55] Jiang Y, Wang P C, Locascio L. E., et al. (2001). Integrated plastic microfluidic devices with ESI-MS for drug screening. *Analytical Chemistry, 73,* 2048-2053.

[56] Glasgow I. K., Beebee D. J. and White V. E. (1999). Design rules for polyimide solvent bonding. *Sensors and Materials, 11,* 269-278.

[57] Paulus, A. and Williams, S. (1998). Integrated capillary electrophoresis using glass and plastic chips. *Proc. SPIE Microfluidic Devices, 3515,* 94-103.

[58] Laurie Brown, Terry Koerner, J. Hugh Horton. (2006). Fabrication and characterization of poly (methylmethacrylate) microfluidic devices bonded using surface modifications and solvents. *Lab Chip, 6,* 66-73.

[59] Junshan Liu, Hongchao Qiao, Chong Liu,et al. (2009). Plasma assisted thermal bonding for PMMA microfluidic chips with integrated metal microelectrodes. *Sensors and Actuators B: Chemical, 141,* 646-651;

[60] Chong Liu, Jing-Min Li, Jun-Shan Liu, et al. (2009). Fracture mechanism of metal electrode integrated on a chip and fabrication of a poly(ethylene terephthalate) electrophoresis microchip. *Talanta, 79,* 1341-1347.

[61] J M Li, C Liu, X D Dai, et al. (2008). PMMA microfluidic devices with three-dimensional features for blood cell filtration. *J. Micromech. Microeng., 18,* 095021.

[62] J.M. Li, C. Liu, J.S. Liu, et al. (2009). Multi-layer PMMA microfluidic chips with channel networks for liquid sample operation. *J. Materials Processing Technology, 209,* 5487-5493.

[63] P. B. Koeneman, I. J. Busch-Vishniac and K. L. Wood. (1997). Feasibility of micropower supplies for MEMS. *J. Microelectromechnical Systems, 6,* 355-362.

[64] J. B. Lee, Z. Chen, M. G. Allen, et al. (1995). A Miniaturized High-Voltage Solar Cell Array as an Electrostatic MEMS Power Supply. *J. Microelectromechnical Systems, 4,* 102-108.

[65] J.Yeom, G. Z. Mozsgai, B. R. Flachsbart, et al. (2005). Microfabrication and characterization of a silicon-based millimeter scale, PEM fuel cell operating with hydrogen, methanol, or formic acid. *Sensors and Actuators B: Chemical, 107,* 882-891.

[66] K.Wozniak, D.Johansson, M. Bring, et al. (2004). A micro direct methanol fuel cell demonstrator. *J. Micromech. Microeng., 14,* S59-S63.

[67] H. Guo and A. Lal. (2003). Nanopower betavoltaic microbatteries. Proc. 12th Int. Conf. Solid State Sensors, Actuators and Microsystems, Boston, US, 36-39.

[68] S. S. Hsieh, J. K. Kuo, C. F. Hwang, et al. (2004). A novel design and microfabrication for a micro PEMFC. *Microsystem Technologies*, 10, 121-126.

[69] M.Noponen, T. Mennola, M.Mikkola, et al. (2002). Measurement of current distribution in a free-breathing PEMFC. *J. Power Sources, 106,* 304-312.

[70] T. Hottinen, O. Himanen, P. Lund. (2004). Effect of cathode structure on planar free-breathing PEMFC. *J. Power Sources, 138*, 205-210.

[71] T.Mennola, M.Mikkola, M. Noponen, et al. (2002). Measurement of ohmic voltage losses in individual cells of a PEMFC stack. *J. Power Sources, 112,* 261-272.

[72] Eiichi Sakaue. Micromachining/nanotechnology in direct methanol fuel cell. (2005). 18th IEEE International Conference on Micro Electro Mechanical Systems. January 30~February 3, Fontainebleau Hilton Resort, Miami Beach, Florida, US.

[73] J. Han and E. Park. (2002). Direct methanol fuel-cell combined with a small back-up battery. *J. Power Sources, 112,* 477-483.

[74] A. K. Shuksla, M. K. Ravikumar, M. Neergat, et al. (1999). A 5W liquid-feed solid-polymer-electrolyte direct methanol fuel cell stack with stainless steel. *J. Applied Electrochemistry, 29,*129-132.

[75] K.Scott, P.Argyropoulos and K.Sundmacher. (1999). A model for the liquid feed direct methanol fuel cell. *J. Electroanalytical Chemistry, 477,* 97-110.

[76] D. H. Jung, S. Y. Cho, D. H. Peck, et al. (2002). Performance evaluation of a Nafion/silicon oxide hybrid membrane for direct methanol fuel cell. *J. Power Sources, 106,* 173-177.

[77] U. Krewer, Y. Song, K. Sundmacher, et al. (2004). Direct methanol fuel cell (DMFC): analysis of residence time behavior of anodic flow bed. *Chemical Engineering Science, 59,* 119-130.

[78] S. Gupta, S. Mahapatra, J. Datta. (2004). A potential anode material for the direct alcohol fuel cell. *Journal of Power Sources, 131,* 169-174.

[79] W. Zhou, B. Zhou, W. Li, et al. (2004). Performance comparison of low-temperature direct alcohol fuel cells with different anode catalysts. *J. Power Sources, 126,* 16-22.

[80] T. Kobayashi, J. Otomo, C. Wen, et al. (2003). Direct alcohol fuel cell—relation between the cell performance and the adsorption of intermediate originating in the catalyst-fuel combinations. *J.Power Sources, 124,* 34-39.

[81] S. Song, G. Wang, W. Zhou, et al. (2005). The effect of the MEA preparation procedure on both ethanol crossover and DEFC performance. *J. Power Sources, 140,* 103-110.

[82] J. Yeom, G.Z. Mozsgai, B.R. Flachsbart, et al. (2003). A Silicon Microfabricated Direct Formic Acid Fuel Cell. *ASME Fuel Cell Science, Engineering and Technology Proceedings,* 267-272.

[83] Yimin Zhu, Su Y. Ha and Richard I. Masel. (2004). High power density direct formic acid fuel cells. *Journal of Power Sources, 130,* 8-14.

[84] S. Ha, B. Adams and R.I. Masel. (2004). A miniature air breathing direct formic acid fuel cell. *J.Power Sources, 128,* 119-124.

[85] C. Ricea, S. Ha, R. I. Masel, et al. (2002). Direct formic acid fuel cells. *J. Power Sources, 111,* 83-89.

[86] M. M. Mench, H. M. Chance and C. Y. Wang. (2004). Direct Dimethyl Ether Polymer Electrolyte Fuel Cells for Portable Applications. *J. Electrochemical Society, 151,* 144-150.

[87] M. Madou. (1997). Fundamentals of Microfabrication, CRC Press, Boca Raton, FL.

[88] Jing rong Yu, Ping Cheng, Zhiqi Ma, et al. (2003). Fabrication of a miniature twin-fuel-cell on silicon wafer. *Electrochimica Acta., 48,* 1537-1541.

[89] Jingrong Yu, Ping Cheng, Zhiqi Ma, et al. (2003). Fabrication of miniature silicon wafer fuel cells with improved performance. *J. Power Sources, 124,* 40-46.

[90] Zhiyong Xiao, Guizhen Yan, Chunhua Feng, et al. (2006). A silicon-based fuel cell micro power system using a microfabrication technique. *J. Micromech. Microeng., 16,* 2014-2020.

[91] Keyur Shah, W. C. Shin and R. S. Besser. (2004). A PDMS micro proton exchange membrane fuel cell by conventional and non-conventional microfabrication techniques. *Sensors and Actuators B: Chemical, 97,* 157-167.

[92] Siew Hwa Chan, Nam-Trung Nguyen, et al. (2005). Development of a polymeric micro fuel cell containing laser-micromachined flow channels. *J. Micromech. Microeng., 15,* 231-236.

[93] J. Wind, R. Spah, W.Kaiser. (2002). Metallic bipolar plates for PEM fuel cells. *J. Power Sources, 105,* 256-260.

[94] Shuo-Jen Lee, Yu-Pang Chen and Ching-Han Huang. (2005). Electroforming of metallic bipolar plates with micro-featured flow field. *J. Power Sources, 145,* 369-375.

[95] Atul Kurmar, R.G.Reddy. (2003). Modeling of polymer electrolyte membrane fuel cell with metal foam in the flow-field of the bipolarlend plates. *J. Power Sources, 114,* 54-62.

[96] J.S.Liang, C. Liu and L.J.Sun. (2009). A Silicon Micro Direct Methanol Fuel Cell Demonstrator using. *Materials Science Forum, 628-629,* 423-428.

[97] L.J. Sun, J.S. Liang, C. Liu, et al. (2009). Effects of the initial stencil width on stainless steel wet chemical etching: combined model and experimental investigations. *J. Micromech. Microeng.,* 19, 085023.

[98] M.M. Li, J.S. Liang, C. Liu, et al(2009). Effects of Anode Flow Field Design on CO2 Bubble Behavior in μDMFC. *Sensors,* 9, 3314-3324.

INDEX

N

P